MUSHy PEAS
ON TOAST

MUSHY PEAS ON TOAST

Laurian Clemence

PAN MACMILLAN

First published 2008
by Pan Macmillan South Africa
Private Bag X19
Northlands
2116

www.panmacmillan.co.za

ISBN: 978-1-77010-067-1

Cover design: Donald Hill of Blue Apple
Design and layout: Triple M Design
Printed and bound in South Africa by
Pinetown Printers

For my parents,
Mum, Dad and Rolf.

And for the dude who invented camembert cheese.

Mum, I hope your mates don't get hold of this.

CHAPTER ONE

THE END

Crisis.

Not many books start at the end. This one does.

Anthony – my long-term boyfriend and possible paternal candidate to our two perfect children – and I broke up last night. It's been in the offing for at least a year now. This is the man I met over tequila shooters at a bar in first-year varsity. He walked up to me, thrust a Magic Marker into my hand and demanded that I write my phone number on his shirt. He also hung a gigantic poster from his bedroom window, which the whole of my residence could plainly see: 'Peas on Toast, Room 929, this is my number: 065 555 4321'.

I'd found the love of my life. And for five and a half years, I truly believed I'd taken the easy road: no endless dating, no uncertainty – we were a unit. As an only child, I suffer endless hang-ups, one of them is the fear of being alone. My parents' divorce ten years ago heightened this abandonment issue. I didn't enjoy being an only child; I remember constantly asking my parents to create some siblings. Discovering a companion in Anthony – a partner in crime, someone who was with me through everything – filled me with security, but the safety eventually became too stifling. At this point, my friends are leaps ahead of me in the Independence Arena.

The only child bit is terribly important, as was my parents' divorce. Although the break up yesterday was what I imagined to be the worst day of my life, it was actually only the fourth worst day of my life.

Worst Day of My Life: Months from now I'll be sitting on a couch day-in, day-out, chain-smoking and feeling triple the amount of heartache I presently feel.

Second Worst Day of My Life: My parents' split – the day before my final Biology exam in Matric (a massive explosion of tears and screaming).

Third Worst Day of My Life: It hasn't happened yet, but I presume – at least at this very moment – it will be when Anthony's gametes fuse with another woman's to form a foetus.

Fourth Worst Day of My Life: My and Anthony's split. About twelve hours ago.

Thirteenth Worst Day of My Life: I'm not sure yet. But there definitely is one.

The problem is that Anthony fashioned me into your classic co-dependent semi-spouse. This was as much my fault as it was his. Latching onto the White Picket Fence dream at such a young age was probably not the wisest thing to do but we only ever see these things in retrospect, don't we?

From the outset, Anthony was terribly romantic. A dreamy character with soulful hazel eyes, he'd gaze at me, adoringly. The Gaze would make my heart stop; even at the end.

We started off together in Cape Town as student lovers, which was easy. Fun. Once he even convinced me to walk up Devil's Peak with him – and I don't walk. I don't do anything that is physically exerting. During our time together, we worked in America, backpacked around Thailand and parts of Africa, and toured Europe. Then we relocated to Johannesburg, moved into an apartment, and suddenly it was toilet seat up-or-down ... We moved to Jo'burg for the same reason almost everyone does: job opportunities. I got a job as a reporter and he worked at a large bank. I suppose that the domesticity of it all got a bit much for us. Slowly but surely, we started to unravel. Sadly.

Anthony was my everything. Our lives were planned out to the tiniest detail. This, I believe, was the first mistake. We had intended to move to San Francisco the following year, marry at twenty-eight, and then I'd pop out two perfect spawn – we'd even picked out names for our unborn children. How ridiculous is that? Now, with all of these plans gone, it feels as though I've been hurled into a black hole. I can't imagine my life without him and I don't even know if we'll remain in contact; I don't know anything right now. Wait, I do know one little thing and that is: I made the right decision. I know this. So, although I'm completely grief-stricken, I know that this moment had to happen. I had to end it.

I think Anthony and I stopped loving each other way before last night. This very man, who drives me nuts with both rage and passion, was expelled from our shared apartment in a fit of tears last night by yours truly. Anthony is a sentimental creature, and I believe that he's also in shock over our undoing. He, the quintessential partner, adored and practically adopted by my mum, respected and held at arm's length by my eccentric and flighty dad, is now My Ex-Boyfriend. Anthony the Ex. Ex Anthony.

For the first time since I was nineteen years old, I'm without a boyfriend. I never considered that this would happen to me. This was supposed to be *it*. We were that lucky couple, sweethearts who'd found each other at a young age. And we loved each other right from the start. A dizzy, overpowering, lusty love, where I'd physically ache if he left to go on business for just a week. It was done, my life was mapped out. Our careers were important to us, but we took our relationship just as seriously. Perhaps too seriously. Did this contribute to our downfall? Maybe I got restless, antsy? Was there too much passion? I am, after all, a drama queen, a chaos finder. Did I cause this whole mess? God, I hate myself.

I know I can't blame myself entirely. Anthony is a moody bastard and we knew how to press each other's buttons.

'I hate it when you squeeze the toothpaste from the top, Anthony.'

'Well, do you really have to leave your heels lying all over the place? Wherever I go, I see stupid shoes. God help me, they're fucking everywhere ...'

'Then perhaps move your golf clubs. Or do they now form part of the lounge décor?'

'I'll move the clubs when you move your potentially lethal shoes that could go through my foot like a stake at any time!'

'Do you have to watch cricket with your hand resting on your crotch? It's *Gray's Anatomy* now, anyway.'

'I buy you flowers and you won't let me watch cricket for six hours? How selfish can a person get? You ungrateful wench.'

'Buying me flowers doesn't negate hogging the television for six straight hours.'

'Screw this, I'm going out.'

'Good, don't wake me when you come back.'

Okay, admittedly, it's not the cosiest domestic picture that I'm painting, but still, I'm in total shock. I made him leave. I made him leave! How did we get to this point? I have fifty-three love letters from him in a box under the bed. That tangible evidence of our mutual love doesn't just disappear. As pathetic as it sounds, I was his Mookie and he was my Pookie, and now I'll never hear those words used again. ('Pookie, when last did you do the dishes, you lazy schmuck?' 'Yesterday, Mookie, you intolerable cow.')

Don't think that just because we had such a volatile relationship it was always vile. It wasn't. There was also: 'Mookie, I love you more than anything on Earth. I can't wait to have mini-Mookies with you.' And, 'Pookie, the pain of childbirth will be worth it just to breed with you.'

And this is what I'm remembering now. Over the past forty-eight hours, I have smoked sixty Marlboro Lights, drunk two bottles of sauvignon blanc, watched three omnibuses of *Home and Away* and been dragged to a stupid Cameron Diaz chick flick by my mother in the hope that it would stop my incessant crying. Yet, I wept throughout the coffee outing at Vida e Caffé in Greenside too. Right there on the pavement.

'Peas, it's going to be all right.'

'No, it's really not. Ever again.'

'Perhaps you're right. I admit I thought you two would be married by next year. You're twenty-five years old now; your biological clock is tick-ticking away.'

Mum starts to choke up. Oh Christ. Mum makes a garbled unfeminine sound.

Another wave of tears.

This is not so much a break up as it is a divorce. We grew to dislike each other quite exceptionally over the last couple of months, and splitting up really was our only choice. Otherwise we would have completely destroyed each other. So, he took his CDs, piled them into his gold Audi A3 – the same car I chose with him in Lenasia Extension 13, the same car I blithely pranged while he was on business in Frankfurt – and moved back in with his parents.

The thing with break ups is that the news spreads around like the trash in tabloids. I have never failed at anything in my life – I'm an only child; we're conditioned to succeed purely because there is no sibling back-up – and this relationship is a failure. People finding out, especially in Jo'burg, where everyone in their mid-twenties knows almost everybody else, is bound to be humiliating. I know that people were hedging bets on when we'd get married. Now we've gotten divorced before we even got married – something I'd prefer, at the ripe old age of twenty-five, to scratch from my Relationship Curriculum Vitae.

If anybody had been eavesdropping on our breakup, they'd think we were quite pathetic. I know I would.

'Mookie, I'll always love you ...'

'Me too, Pookie. But you really need to leave now. Please ... just go.'

In the meantime, I'm struggling to keep my job on track while everything around me falls apart. I'm a full-time journalist at *Good Food* magazine. A bloody good journalist, thank you very much, even if *they* don't realise it. I may write about cilantro and meatballs in wine coulis and the best freshly squeezed *jus d'orange* in town, but I try to take it seriously. At least one day a week anyway.

I skipped work for two days after the break up. My slave-driver editor, ever unsympathetic, wasn't buying it.

'I have a stomach bug.'

'That's nice. Your feature on radish supreme is due today.'

'I'm inconveniently plagued with diarrhoea, though. I can't come in.'

'Write it on the company toilet, Peas; we have a deadline.'

'No. I can't, really.' Choking back tears, I put the phone down and left it to fate.

Besides, I couldn't let the sub-editor, my nemesis, otherwise known as The Sub, know the truth. I could just imagine her popping the champagne cork at news of my bereavement.

To the general public, I'm citing that we broke up because of irreconcilable differences. I need to make plans on how to handle this, despite feeling as though I'm dying of a terminal disease. Break ups aren't just 'Goodbye, it's been real.' There's a snowball effect. Actually, it's more like an avalanche. Everything else shifts forcefully to accommodate it. The tides of human emotion, furniture and, of course, living arrangements.

I don't want to move. Middle-class, cosmopolitan Illovo, a suburb nestled in between Rosebank and Sandton, suits me just fine. It mostly comprises old, seventies-style apartment blocks and shops all within walking distance of the door of my large, solid old-school flat. Sure, the shower breaks every month and the kitchen is finished with a dark shag-pad varnish, but this is my home and I love it. I'll be damned if I have to move to the outer suburb of Fourways into a Tuscan box surrounded by car dealerships. That would be a fate worse than death. Pookie felt the same way.

I just got off the phone with his mother. We bawled incomprehensible sentences, so I'm not sure what was said – we couldn't understand each other through all that wailing. Some might be relieved not to have to deal with their in-laws anymore, but not me. His family is like my own.

This is all rather devastating. I've been with this man for most of my twenties – how does one remember to be alone, never mind live alone?

Luckily, my Italian friend Giulia has said she'd move in with me. She's been anticipating this break up since 2001, I believe. Lizzy, my other best friend, said she's relieved because she was dreading wearing a meringue bridesmaid special although I never would have done that to her. I'm not sure she understands how detrimental this break up is to my health as Lizzy has never been in a long-term commitment before. All the same, my friends are trying their best to be supportive.

> LIZZY: Dude, are you coping? I'm bringing round some wine, which we can smash immediately. Get out the glasses!

> GIULIA: I'll be over straight after gym. Are you eating? I'll cook pasta. Make sure you have pomodoro sauce. Is there any food in your house? Okay. Never mind. I'm on it.

> CONNOR: Can I bring you a tramezzini? I've told my boss you're a mental patient so he'd let me leave work to drop it off and make sure you're not straight-caning Smirnoff Red directly from the bottle.

IS THIS WHAT DEATH FEELS LIKE?

It's Day Five. Apparently I'll only stop crying in two weeks, or so says Tracey Cox, the author of *Hot Love*. This is the worst pain I have ever felt. I want Pookie back. But I must remind myself that in reality I couldn't stand to be with irritating, annoying Pookie for one more day. I hope my friends don't run out of patience; I'm not nearly done crying yet.

I've forgotten what it feels like to feel normal. And to think that I'd even imagined Ant's perfect proposal one day on Phi Phi Island as he hinted he'd like to do. How could I give that up? Pass me a bucket. I'm going to throw up.

I'm all alone. In an apartment spanning a hundred square metres there is all this space to stumble around in, yet I take up all of two measly metres (including heels). Most often, I'm lying on the couch watching *Seinfeld* reruns. I wonder if Mrs Goldberg upstairs heard the commotion before the break up. We did throw a few random items at each other before we said our final 'I love yous'. She probably wonders why it's so quiet now, barring *Lionel Richie's Greatest Hits*, of course. I hate being alone for even one second so need to fill the silence with music. Giulia's going to move in soon. Thank God! It's just that she has to break it gently to her Italian father. They don't want her to leave the nest – ever – and they're distraught she's thinking of *actually* moving out. She has no idea how much I need her to right now.

Yesterday I unglued my swollen eyes, dragged myself to the office and even managed to write a feature at work about braised duck with carrots julienne. I haven't told my colleagues yet about my relationship failure. I don't want to give them an excuse to see my work as below par, especially the editor who shot me a look of absolute disdain when I walked in today.

Anthony called me last night. He wanted to meet up for a chat. I agreed, but wasn't particularly gagging to meet up so soon – I mean, I've only just stopped crying enough to exit my apartment to buy milk. But, we met up at swanky Bleu, a pretentious French restaurant, and talked about where to go from here. It was awkward:

PEAS: Pookie, I mean *Anthony*, I propose we try and be adults about the fact that we secretly hate each other.

ANTHONY: Mookie, I mean *Peas on Toast* ...

PEAS: Why do you have to include my surname? That's so typical of you. You always have to take it to the next level.

ANTHONY: You started it, Peas on Toast. I hate you.

PEAS: Please just pass the salt.

I guess it was fairly positive, all in all. It could've been intensely emotional, involving tears and such, but it really was bearable. We managed not to throw cutlery at each other, he paid for dinner, and now I feel empty and numb.

Why do I have to go through a break up? I thought I'd managed to astutely avoid this my whole life. What I can't do though, is show the world that I'm dying. My friends know, but I have a reputation to live up to, and being a reputable Party Animal doesn't allow for grieving periods. Del Amitri is playing on the radio – oh shut it up! They're Anthony's favourite group. Everything reminds me of him.

The only thing to do right now, besides sit at home and mope, is to throw myself back into the party scene. I missed out on it so much, being tied down and all, that I need to make up for lost time. I must plant a smile on my face and show the world that I will not be conquered, that I am not a failure. In fact, I'll be even more of a success than I was with Anthony. Surely this positive attitude can only benefit me? Soon I'll attract a new and better long-term boyfriend to replace Anthony and all will be well. I just need to get out there and be amazing.

After The Meeting with Anthony, I did just that. I joined Connor and Bennet at the Jolly Roger, to drink vodka spritzers. This is our local watering hole, an establishment in Parkhurst overlooking 4th Avenue and Northcliff Hill. What on earth would I do without Connor and Bennet? I shudder to think. I love these boys like brothers.

Connor is sensitive with big, Irish, blue eyes and a mop of dark hair, which immediately makes him completely attractive to the opposite sex. Like Hugh Grant, without the foppish quality perhaps. He fancies himself as James Bond, I think. For example, at the entrance to a club, he'll bark, 'I'm not paying to go in there! James Bond would never pay for club entrance, he'd be a VIP.' An aficionado of good taste, he has no problem using face cream, buying collared shirts with high thread count or expensive cabernet sauvignon, and is confident that metrosexual is the new black. Luckily he earns more than enough as a stockbroker to support his expensive tastes. As much as he loves art, fine food and poetry, Connor is also famed for his outlandish drunken exhibitionism during which he'll drop his pants, dive over tables and dress up in ridiculous outfits. He makes friends easily and almost every woman I know in this city wants to date him. Or is in love with him. I find it all rather amusing. We've always just been buddies, and I've never looked at Connor as anything vaguely sexual. We almost snogged once when really drunk, but then just laughed and mutually decided it was a bad idea.

Bennet is into vintage cars. Or so he says. His lime green Ford Cortina doesn't quite fit into what would be described as an expensive antique, but he insists that 'chicks dig it'. He loses his keys frequently when he's out and about. He'll often drag me off the couch and take me out as his wingman so he can charm big-breasted women. Together we plot how he can attain a good shag. Bennet is as much a great appreciator of the shag as, say, Connor is a great appreciator of Pablo Picasso. Bennet and Connor are top-quality men. The three of us make a good team and I absolutely adore them. I met these guys years ago and we have been friends ever since.

In retrospect, maybe going out right after meeting Anthony wasn't such a great idea because now I feel worse, thanks to one too many spritzers after being egged on by Bennet, Connor and many others at the establishment. At 2:00 a.m., in my absolute misery, I phoned Anthony. Not completely sure what I said, but it was something along the lines of:

'Hi, it's me.'

'Humph, what time is it?'

'You sleeping?'

'You drunk?'

'You sleeping?'

'You drunk?'

'How are you?'

'You're pissed.'

'Okay, well you seem to be all right. Just checking in on you.'

'Why you so hammered?'

'I am NOT hammered, for Chrissakes.'

'Goodnight then.'

Two minutes later my phone rang. It was Anthony.

'You driving home?'

'That's right.'

'Well, drive safely. Please.'

'Okay. And like, look after yourself.'

'Did you phone because of our last-call-of-the-day-when-we-aren't-together habit?'

'Might have.'

'Fair enough.'

'It'll end soon.'

'You'll probably get one from me after my hockey dinner this weekend.'

'The coppers – shit. Better go.'

Oh God. I feel terrible. Nobody thinks I'm as amazing as Anthony did. He used to laugh at all my jokes. Even when they weren't funny. But I've got to remember the bad too. He was never good in a crisis. And crises and I go hand in hand. Canadagate is a good example. It occurred when we worked overseas. I was thrown out of Canada for not having the right visa requirements. Organised Anthony, on the other hand, with his British passport, was on the right side of the authorities:

'Why didn't you get the right visa?'

'Because they told me I didn't need one, ferfucksakes.'

'Well maybe you should've double checked!'

'Do you honestly think I didn't double, triple, quadruple check? Are you suggesting I wanted this to happen?'

'Fuck you and fuck your stupid passport. Don't talk to me for five days.'

'Fine. I won't.'

'And one last thing before I start ignoring you ... I hate you.'

'Does it look like I am bothered?'

'Yes, it does. I am more bothered by the fact that WE CAN'T GET INTO CANADA.'

'Focus, Anthony! We're stuck on the St Lawrence River with nothing but a Taco Bell in sight. Let's look at our options. We could try another border post. It may solve this problem.'

'Don't wanna solve this problem.'

'Well I do.'

'I can't hear you.'

Talk about a couple having no conflict-resolution skills.

Later in the day (after sitting in silence in Taco Bell for an hour and a half):

'Okay. I'm ready to go to Buffalo to get you a visa. And by the way, I don't hate you. I love you. I'm sorry for being horrible.'

'Thank you. I love you too, my little Pookie Pooklepop.'

'I love you more.'

'No, I love you more.'

'No, *I* love you more. That's why we're driving across the States to get you a visa.'

'So this is still my fault?'

'Yes.'

All these memories. I'm still overwhelmed by everything, wondering around in a nostalgic, catatonic daze.

PUBLIC DECENCY

It's Helen's birthday party tonight at her estate in the sticks. Although another feminine cog in my immediate circle, Helen is better friends with Lizzy than with me. We've always been around each other (since school), but we've never really been close. However, she's been in a long-term relationship, so would probably understand more than my other friends at the moment. I think the others may be pretending to understand, but to their credit, they're making a good effort. To get my ass off the couch, apply make-up and get into my car is going to take an elephant-sized effort. This is my first social occasion where I'll be alone. One person. Single.

I'm dreading it. I'd rather be tiptoeing around landmine territory than formulate a valid explanation as to why my husband-to-one-day-be isn't on my arm.

Everyone I know will be there, and while some know of the split, it's going to be one of those nights where I have to recount the story forty-five times for everyone's benefit. I am exhausted just thinking about it. Perhaps I should make a speech as I arrive.

(Spoon against glass: ting ting ting ting ting.)

'Sorry. Could I just have everyone's attention? Thanks. I have an announcement to make: Anthony and I have split ... Any questions? No? Okay. Rock on.'

Why do I have to go? I know why. So I won't look and feel like a loser, moping at home, chain smoking, chugging Cape to Rio from the bottle, that sort of thing. I must guard against becoming a hermit. Or even worse: a *recluse*. I'm a self-confessed drama queen who loves being the centre of attention and making people laugh. Becoming a recluse would be devastating.

Just imagine the whispers: 'Peas on Toast has become (gasp!) a ... recluse.'

And tomorrow I'm being dragged to a brunch, a party and a club. As of yet, I haven't nailed myself to a wall in protest, so maybe this means I'm starting to pull myself together. Surely I could get used to this lifestyle – being free again, enjoying the fruits of youth: boys, alcohol and the constant flotsam and jetsam of nightclub living. I haven't seen the sun, the garden or the Rosebank Mall in daylight for a good few days now. In fact, if Jo'burg was bombed tomorrow, I probably wouldn't really notice, except for the loud explosion and perhaps splinters of broken glass in my living room.

But things are looking up.

Giulia, my vivacious Italian friend, is moving in now, for sure. Her father, shedding flamboyant tears, begrudgingly accepted that his supposedly devoutly Catholic daughter is leaving *la casa*. We co-signed the new lease yesterday. This is a step forward. However, she can only move in after Christmas. It's November.

And all of a sudden Anthony needs his half of the deposit back in order to move into a new flat, which I find odd, considering that he's living with his parents now. I can't give it to him until my new flatmate pays me a deposit. As a result, it was reaffirmed today why I cannot be with this person – because he can be so difficult that I just want to throttle him.

Predictably, at Turtle Creek I was asked where Anthony was, by someone I don't even know that well. 'Where is Ant?'

'I don't know where he is. He could be anywhere really.'

'Well, you're his girlfriend, so I thought he'd be here with you.'

'Well, if I was his girlfriend, then maybe.'

'Well ... oh. Nevermind.'

Stupid men. Why even ask?

This morning, however, Anthony tetchily insisted that I move out and accused me of withholding his deposit. ('Mookie, I mean *Peas*. You are withholding my deposit.') Where must I move to? The parking lot of Thrupps Centre, perhaps? He has parents nearby; I don't! And asking my Cape Town-based father for a deposit is out of the question – I'm not sure he's exactly financially stable. If I had it, just to shut him up, I would give it to him. The crises seem to continue even though we're not together anymore. It's ridiculous.

In the meantime, being suddenly single feels as though I have an invisible sign around my neck saying, 'Open For Business'. Or so it would appear. I'm being asked out by men that seem to suddenly have emerged from the social woodwork and, quite frankly, I'm not up for putting on my face and heels just yet. Although, in some way, it is boosting my flagging ego which Anthony used to prop up. Suddenly men are interested in me, now that my ball and chain has disappeared. Is there a secret signal that single woman emit unconsciously? Is it like a high-pitched dog whistle that only men can pick up? I can't remember the last time I was chatted up, it was that long ago. See? Everything's going to be alright – soon I'll have a new boyfriend, and then I can go back to being looked after. I can't wait.

Well, I reckon I'll be ready in a few weeks' time, maybe. I still feel a sharp stab of pain when I think of Anthony. The pain makes me feel asexual and completely disinterested in anything with a penis. It makes the future seem dismal, all my plans ripped up by their roots. I just can't believe he's gone. He's finally gone.

STARFISHING

It's been two weeks and one day since Anthony and I threw in the towel. The world is empty and dull. I'm slowly getting used to waking up alone and have even started starfishing in our – pardon me – *my* queen-size bed. I feel as if I spawned out of my own body this morning. Delivering myself into the evil hole of debauchery has done me the world of good. I've started to behave badly and this is a good sign. I am socialising, drinking and going out. Giulia gave me a pious look when I gleefully explained to her how I was filling my time, as if she disapproves of my behaviour. This annoyed me, because she still has a serious boyfriend. She's forgotten what it like is to be single and alone.

Nevertheless, I lost Drunken Monopoly on Friday night. I only managed to buy two stations. And I behaved badly because I drank too much wine. The problem with games like Monopoly and such is that I become fiercely competitive. I need to win *everything*.

'Who invited Peas?' was the general sentiment at the end of the evening.

I did, however, manage to attain two properties, the brown ones, for all my cash, through an extortionate auction. This didn't sit well with me, so I got drunk and blew off steam at Bennet for stealing Eloff Street.

The physical effect of my rash and rapidly changing lifestyle is plainly visible. If I am to find my Long-Lost Love amongst this disorder, he's going to have to love me for my personality. Within the past two-week period, I've transformed into a zitbag and have lost two kilos. I am a naturally thin person – yes, lucky me. Now I just look gaunt and malnourished. On the bright side, I'm taking extra care to wear shirts that encourage a ball-busting cleavage. I'm still crying in short spurts, and I'm feeling terribly sorry for myself because I feel a strange desperation that needs constant love and attention from other people.

I'm lying face down on my bed hoping that when I open my eyes, I'll miraculously find myself in a far-flung place like Norway or the Falkland Islands. Life in these places may border on dull or cultur-ally obscene, but I wouldn't turn that down right now. People who break up with their partners there probably don't drink through the pain like people do here. They probably just hit the endive farm, hoe a little, and then feel better.

Strangely, I'm not lonely. I'm more certain than ever that I made the right decision with Anthony, but I still have no idea what to do at this point. I need plans. I need control. It terrifies me that I have to make plans on my own. At least, for now. I need to find an iden-tity again. After being with Anthony for so long – living together, doing each other's laundry, considering him in every decision, my individual identity somehow got lost along the way. Apparently you only find yourself when you're alone, which is terrifying. I have to face it though – I am one in this world. Perhaps I should start at the beginning. I am Peas. What do I stand for? I don't know. Perhaps I should just start with the letter 'P'. That's easier.

P is for:

Peas on Toast – An unsavoury savoury English meal. Or a 25-year-old journalist who manages to cause her own chaos just by opening her mouth.

Poen – A name for a cookie, a geschmutzen, a fnoo, a punani.

Pissoir – French vernacular for place in which to spend a penny. The toilet.

Pleated jeans – An eighties profanity.

Pull – To suck face. One needs to 'go on the ...' in order to come right.

Penis – A willy. A man can act like one.

Paris – My mother's family hails from Paris. I am therefore half French. I do enjoy a good piece of garlic, yes. I even speak the language.

Pneumonia – Excessive and dangerous levels of fluid in the alveoli of the lungs, often started off by chronic bronchitis. I had this last year.

Psycho – A person (axe murderers, stalkers, that sort of thing) who, in previous times, would have had to undergo a frontal lobotomy due to often sociably inept behavioural patterns, and/or the hearing of voices in one's head.

Penile Erectile Dysfunction – A condition when the willy won't stand. Hugh Hefner sorted his out by using Viagra, his 'favourite recreational drug'.

Planter's wart – A fungal thing that grows roots on the bottom of one's foot when one doesn't wear flip-flops in the showers at boarding school.

Pretty – Only used to its maximum potential when a Cape Flats local screams, 'Hey prittie, show me some pantie' at you.

Pie-eater – A particularly rotund person who eats pies in monolithic quantities.

Pants – Trousers. Or when something is considered bullshit, then it's pants.

Punjabi MC – A cool Indian fellow who mixes bhangra and doof doof, hailing from Lenz Extension 13.

Poenda, The – A town in the sticks with a refinery, where the streets are still named after Apartheid architects like Hendrik

Verwoerd, and there are a crap load of mines. Where Hendrik, Giulia's boyfriend, unwittingly found himself a job as an engineer.

Porsche – A fancy car, German engineered. But I'd turn one down for a 2.0 litre turbo Audi A3. It's just my personal taste.

Prunella Scales – Cybil, wife of Basil, in *Fawlty Towers*.

Pietermaritzburg – Where I was extracted, via C-section, from my mother's uterus. Apparently has the highest drinking rate per capita *in the world*, before Vegas, before Moscow. Followed closely by Grahamstown, or so I'm told. At R2 for two shots on Commercial Road, one can imagine why.

Pearls – Old money.

Plastic – New money.

Pearl necklace – When someone jizzes between yer tits.

Perky – Why I love my B cups.

Phuck – Gangsta talk for 'fuck'.

Phat – Not rotund, cool.

Purgatory – Us Catholics find ourselves here when we've had sex before marriage. It's not a nice place, or so the Pope reckons.

Phil (of the Collinses) – Makes good karaoke music, but throw a hairdryer in the bath while you're at it.

Peace – What people have been shooting and bombing each other for to find, since forever. Often blame religion in order to justify.

Putaine – Bitch in French.

Porous – Paris Hilton's koppel.

Plastered – When a wall is smeared with concrete, smoothed over and painted. Or when one is blotto.

Procreation – Necessary sex for the survival of our species.

Primi Piatti – An Italian restaurant chain where waiters take your order on scooters and wear orange overalls. Make fruity jam jars filled with enough vodka to annihilate a pregnant goat.

Porn – Voyeuristic sexual acts, played out in front of a camera. Not for under-eighteens.

Porno – A Natal word for dodgy.

Pérignon, Dom – What I drank on Saturday night.

Prophylaxis – Anti-malarial tablets. Side effects include mental instability and physical discomfort. I experienced the latter, with my fingernails falling out, as well as extreme photosensitivity, making me look like Rudolf the Reindeer for three weeks.

Pina Colada – Cocktail made from rum and pineapple. Not only do I drink these in the pouring rain, I drink them in the sun, and in the back of cars. Especially lately.

Patricia Lewis – Hails from Glenvista, Jo'burg South, once did soft German porn flick (*Schneller! Mein kleinen apfelstrudel, schneller!*), has yellow hair, owns an extraordinary amount of leopard-print unitards, was Miss Southgate back in the eighties, had a public media argument with her nemesis, Amor Vittone (*You* Magazine, March 2005), and can be heard on her latest album, *Bok Treffers Sestien*.

Pooh – Something boys do.

Prick – A dude with a small knob. And who compensates with a 5 series BMW.

Plutonium – Symbol Pt. One tablespoon of Pt placed on the side of the road in Brits will kill everyone in Johannesburg, never mind those unfortunate enough to live in Brits itself. My science teacher told me so. Radiation poisoning is something epic: if you're stupid enough to pick up that spoonful of plutonium, the skin on your hand will turn translucent, you'll see all the way through to the bone, then your hand self-implodes, then you, like, die of cancer.

That's good start, right?

BACK ON THE WAGON

I am back in the dating game. After just a month. This has taken even me by surprise. I officially got lucky on Saturday – smooch lucky. With a guy called Hansel. Handsome Hansel is Austrian. It happened in a dark corner of Manhattan, a place for drunk, single people.

If he's sensible, he won't phone me again. But it's all right if he isn't sensible, I feel like a little roll in the hay, actually. I miss intimacy and am sick of hugging a bottle in order to find some.

However, a month on from our unofficial divorce, I have hit my first getting-over-Anthony obstacle. He's going on a date with someone from his bloody polo club. Apparently, as Bennet claims, but I take this information with a pinch of salt, she has a moustache. So I'm not going to blow the fireworks they potentially have out of proportion. Plus she swings a polo mallet around. A moustached mallet-swinging bird. I will not panic.

It does, however, feel like I've been impaled in the stomach with a blunt instrument. When I first heard the news, I couldn't breathe for an hour. My colleague Dierdra had to take me to the Radium Beer Hall during lunch for a double gin and tonic. Needless to say, after another two gins, I started breathing normally again.

It sorted me out because I'm reeling with resentment. I will now date with a vengeance. Guilt-free. I worried for a brief second that Anthony would feel hurt that I'm already dating, but if he's out on the prowl then I'd better get out there too – even if I'm not quite ready. There's no way he's allowed to move on before I do. That is way too humiliating. Last night I went out with Austrian Hansel to prove to myself that I'm now really on the market.

Lizzy had an opinion about it, as always. Giulia and Lizzy are my ultimate confidantes. I've known Lizzy since high school and she's good to have around, especially since she knows most of Jo'burg really well. She always makes me giggle, and is always severely practical. Like Giulia, she'll always give me an honest slap on the shoulder. Everybody loves Lizzy. She grew up on a maize farm, so prefers to run around barefoot, but, when necessary, dolls herself up for a night on the town. She is my co-conspirator, and my party image wouldn't be nearly as reputable without Lizzy at my side. We drink wine together, laugh like hyenas, and usually find ourselves at the centre of a party, any party, anywhere.

PEAS: 'I'm still dying but I've decided to date Hansel.'

LIZZY: 'You're not dying, drama queen. You're being wined and dined by an Austrian. Do you even like him?'

PEAS: 'It's only because I need intimacy right now.'

LIZZY: 'Peas, I haven't had intimacy in four months and I'm all right. Now dry your eyes, put on your good underwear, and only bring him home if you're honestly ready. And for God's sake, be careful, you know that Europeans don't ... bathe regularly.'

PEAS: 'Fine. So much for sympathy. And I am ready. Anthony's dating, so I should be too. So don't worry, you don't have to feel sorry for me anymore.'

LIZZY: 'Maybe you should just come out with me and the girls instead?'

PEAS: 'But this guy could be my future husband, you never know!'

LIZZY: 'Oh fuck. You're so far from ready it's frightening.
PEAS: 'Why would you say that?'

Got to bed at 2:00 a.m. It was a good date, if good dates are based on excellent conversation (we both appreciate Byzantine architecture), good wine and him not asking me when I plan to become his girlfriend, so lessening the pressure. Hansel was an Aryan supermodel, in a Bavarian sort of way. Charming, funny, delightful in fact, with blue eyes, pallid complexion and blond hair. Not usually what I go for.

I decided halfway through our meal that Lizzy might be right – I can't just assume that every guy who asks me out from now on will be compatible with me or want me to be his girlfriend.

Hansel called me after the date as I was driving home. His family is from Salzburg. That's what he phoned to tell me. He ended the conversation by singing 'The Hills are Alive with the Sound of Music'. He's different, I'll give him that much. And it felt great that he was so obviously interested in me. Perhaps Austrians are the unofficial best medicine for unofficial divorcees like myself. Or perhaps I'm just losing my unofficial mind.

I'm trying my best to be blasé about my break up and pretend that I'm so over it. My moping was beginning to bore me. I've been with the Salzburger for a whole week, but am honestly wondering whether I'll make it through another date. *Why?* I'm still trying to catch up with my friends' youthful lifestyle. It's starting to become rather fun, being irresponsible and on the same wavelength as my friends. Amongst irregular smatterings of Anthony wobblies, I'm pulling myself out of my dark little hole to emerge as a quasi-functional human being who can be let loose into public spaces on a pro rata basis.

KARAOKE AND LOUDNESS

Giulia has started moving her stuff in. This is tremendously uplifting. At least she's seen me waltz around in my underpants and doesn't take offence when I watch *Home and Away* in them. She doesn't care much for my daily Australian white-trash soapie fix, but then I don't care much for her daily dose of the Italian channel, RAI Mondo, so fair is fair. I can't wait to have her around to cook me pasta and to polish off vintage wine together. I should've done this years ago – we're going to be just like Rachel and Monica in *Friends*!

Last night after work I decided to host my first get-together at our apartment, in lieu of Giulia's arrival. It feels good to actually want to celebrate something again. The girls came round for a stint of karaoke and binge drinking. This is our shtick and we make a lot of noise. We're your average sort of girls, but also loud and opinionated and inclined to steal the thunder from everyone else in a room if we're in public. If we're not singing into the microphone, we're usually arguing about which song we're going to sing:

GIULIA: 'Oh God, not Michael Bolton's "Time, Love and Tenderness" again. Please God no.'

PEAS: 'Why not? It's a classic.'

GIULIA: 'No, it is not.'

LIZZY: 'Right, I'm claiming *Dirty Dancing*.'

PEAS: 'That's a fantastic idea.'

GIULIA: 'How about some Andrea Boccelli?'

LIZZY AND PEAS: 'You can't sing to that.'

Friday evenings have become ritualistic. After a few drinks and karaoke we usually head off to a party, as on this night. Just my luck, though; Anthony was there. I sort of knew he might be and, as raw as I felt, I figured it would be fine. What a stupid misconception.

When I saw him, my heart sank to the bottom of my shoes. And since he knows me so well, he could tell I was trying to hide it. I was, however, relieved at not having invited Hansel along. I don't want a tag-along right now. Even if he sings me Austrian lullabies. He's not my boyfriend, and on a night like this it would've been a disaster.

I chatted to Anthony very briefly along the lines of 'you're coping, I'm coping right?' Then I abruptly headed to the punch tub.

Bennet, as he tends to do, arrived in a whirlwind of lateness.

'I have a huge favour to ask you.'

PEAS: (Cautiously sipping on spilling-over punch glass.) 'What?'

BENNET: (Feverishly groping for a beer from the fridge.) 'My car has broken down, and I'm too hammered to go and fetch it. Can you take me there?'

PEAS: 'Where'd you walk from?'

Bennet: 'Parkmore.' (We're in Bryanston, a good hour's walk away.)

PEAS: 'Gee, let me think about this. No.' (A minute later.) 'Fine then, if you insist.'

It was raining buckets outside, and my perfectly coiffed hair was looking less than beautiful. As for my high heels – schoolboy error – they got wedged into the thick mud like golf tees.

Once we got to his lime-green Ford Cortina, I stood on the side of the road in my heels and a low-cut top resembling a lady of the night while Bennet fiddled with his carburettor. He was shocked several times by the said carburettor, leaving him somewhat catatonic. I smoked a cigarette and got drenched while I pondered the ridiculousness of the situation.

At midnight, Anthony called. He'd left the party at least three hours ago. Or so I'd heard.

'Please, let's just sort everything out, please.'

Drunk and drained, I cried while he talked almost coherently.

He'd been driving around Jo'burg all night to think, weep and fly off the handle. Now he was on his way back from Pretoria after hitting the N1 highway at an indescribable speed in a fit of woe.

PEAS: 'Calm down. Just tell me why you're so hysterical. You have a date for Saturday, you should be just fine.'

ANTHONY: 'I've disinvited my date for Saturday; I don't want to ruin things for us.'

PEAS: 'Why'd you go and do that? I don't think we're ever going to sort "us" out. It's over.'

ANTHONY: 'But even so.'

I then directed him home.

Later, in bed, I considered phoning Hansel to come over, simply because I felt like spooning with someone in a cosy bed. But, in retrospect, I'm glad I didn't. So far, my friends are more than sufficient to keep me occupied.

NEW HOUSEMATE

Giulia is officially my new housemate. I'm so excited I put on my stiletto heels for her big move-in. It's the beginning of a new chapter. Definitely. It has to be. Surely this means things are a-changing? She brought with her a bag of clothes, leftover pasta linguine and three books, and moved into mine and Anthony's old room. I have taken the spare room in the hope of abolishing all association with our relationship. This plan should work nicely.

GIULIA: 'If I'm going to move in ... best you get rid of that ugly vase.'

PEAS: 'You made that for me for my birthday.'

GIULIA: 'Did I?' (Gagging.) 'You sure?'

PEAS: 'Yip.'

GIULIA: 'Oh my God. I'm so sorry.'

Giulia wears cute little suits and killer heels. She's also as Italian as gelato. An Itye. She eats pasta – giant bowls thereof – four times a week, and has started feeding me too. How she stays so svelte is beyond comprehension. When she's happy, excited or angry she shouts. She also shouts at me, quite endearingly, when she thinks I'm being impossible. I've learned not to take it personally. Giulia also manages to fix my crises with the utmost ease. Like the time she hid me in a closet at a company function when I was just about to vomit, or on Friday when she helped me rewrite my 'Rocket? Is it overrated?' feature, because she fancies herself a foodie. She's a management queen, completely suited to her job as an analyst at a small firm. She's worked her way up the corporate ladder rather sterlingly over the last few years. She'll be an excellent companion with which to cohabit.

But, she's going to have to learn how to sing karaoke to *Monster Hits 3*, even though she remains hopeful that the Andrea Boccelli CD she bought me as a gift is a better alternative. I'm not certain if she'll like my strange vocal prowess. As I mentioned, I rather like singing loudly (a habit that Anthony never really came to terms with). It helps me deal with stress. Maybe she'll teach me Italian, so I can sing to Boccelli in the bath. Although chances are she'll regret it considering that she once described my singing as 'a combine harvester scraping over tarmac'. But she hastily added, 'What you lack in voice is made up for by your enthusiasm.' Funny, since her voice sounds like a strangled Italian cat, but I didn't mention this simply to keep the peace.

My first brush with the screaming Italian since she became my housemate happened soon after she moved in. It was Giulia barking to her boyfriend over the telephone: 'Hendrik! What do you *mean* you couldn't get artichokes? … I don't care … don't care … *don't care*. I only told you yesterday morning to get the bloody artichokes for the dish. My father, *merdo*, my *father is going to be distraught*. You don't want to make the fat guy distraught, you know what happens when the fat guy gets angry. Do you understand how dire this is? I promised him you'd deliver the artichokes for his dinner party ... Fuck! Oh and don't you dare make me tell him, oh no no no no ... *you're* going to tell him, my love.'

'Hey, relax,' I said. 'We've got some in the fridge. They're a few weeks old, but they're worth a toss.'

'*Peas*! Are you suggesting, *are you honestly suggesting* ... oh my God, you are serious aren't you? You're actually suggesting I use an ingredient that isn't one hundred per cent fresh for my pappa? Both of you – Hendrik and yourself – should be ashamed of yourselves. Right Hendrik ... are you listening? You need to go to Luigi's Deli ... don't care how late it is ... don't care! Get in your car right now ...'

Don't mess with an Italian and her food. I'm learning fast.

EVEN MEN CAN BE SENSITIVE

Although I am *just fine,* my great friend Connor seems to believe I need some pampering. Having witnessed my bouts of absolute despair over the last two months, he bought me a massage voucher yesterday to cheer me up. Bless him. Connor seems to always know just the right thing to say or do. Sometimes I think he has a telepathic hotwire to my brain. Like when I've had a horrendous day, he'll call because he just seems to sense it.

There's no time like the screwed-up present to have some relieving back-rubbing, so I claimed my present instantly. The haggard-looking masseuse took one look at me and volunteered to do my feet as well.

After twenty minutes of lying on hot stones, my colour had returned and I felt calmer and lighter. Then she analysed my feet.

MASSEUSE: 'You're under some serious stress. Your feet show some major strain.'

ME (with face in mattress): 'Hmmpf uhuh hmmpf.'

MASSEUSE: 'Your liver is suffering, as are your kidneys, and your solar plexus.'

ME: 'Hmmph ... where's my solar plexus?'

MASSEUSE: 'It's the area beneath your heart that carries your emotions. It's basically ... in knots.'

ME: 'Oh dear. That is not good.'

MASSEUSE: 'Do you drink a lot of liquor? I'm feeling a lot of toxins here.'

ME: 'I don't drink alcohol.'

Masseuse: 'Lie all you want, but your solar plexus tells me otherwise.'

I bought some cream from her to balance my solar plexus. It's all about nursing my solar plexus right now. I have solar plexus problems.

AUF WIEDERSEHN, HANSEL

After three dates within a two-week period, I decided to dismiss Hansel, who now has the dubious honour of being The First Guy I Dated After Anthony. Welcome to my Shakespearean tragedy. I feel like a cruel bitch because, for as much as I don't want men to hurt me, I don't like hurting men. I feel intense guilt. I also don't have much experience in 'dumping' men, let's face it.

I hate myself. Mainly because everyone thought he was the best thing since sliced Albany.

Except for Lizzy who commented, 'I didn't think he was all that and a bag of chips.' That's only because he isn't a farmer. Giulia loved Hansel, but then she loves anybody who speaks a foreign language. Anthony hated him, but then I can't expect much else.

ANTHONY: 'So. Who is this kraut you're apparently not seeing?'

PEAS: 'I'm not seeing anyone, and that is derogatory, Anthony.'

ANTHONY: 'Well, my mates seem to think they've seen you around town with some German.'

PEAS: 'A few dates, but it's over now. I'm not ready for a big "thing" yet.'

ANTHONY: 'I am absolutely and crazily upset with you. Why, Peas, why?'

PEAS: 'Pook ... Anthony. It's nothing.'

ANTHONY: 'Well he probably has a farting problem from all the sauerkraut.'

PEAS: 'He's Austrian, not German.'

ANTHONY: 'Does he prance around in *lederhosen* singing "The Hills are Alive"?'

PEAS: 'Actually, yes.'

Dierdra from work introduced me to Hansel, so obviously thinks he's a good guy. Bennet was unsure about me dating again because he'd lose his on-the-jol wingman and my mother was ecstatic about us dating because he's an attorney. Helen, who can talk herself out of any situation and makes contacts in high places, was very impressed by his credentials. He also ate salad, which she said, 'cannot be undermined in men'. Even Connor seemed to like him, and he's usually a sceptic about new men in my life.

'Wow Peas. He may be slightly dilly about his heritage, but he wears merino wool. I'm impressed.'

'You should see his *lederhosen*. But no, Connor, 'fraid not. Merino wool or not, I'm not ready. Perhaps I'm just not that into him.'

'Well then, gud bye, Hansel!'

Hansel is perpetually perfect, so it would seem. But perfect is too good for me presently. Perhaps if I had dated him a year from now, I'd be ready for his perfection. I'm starting to become accustomed to single life, and it's not half bad. But pretending that I am completely baggage-free isn't feasible. Since I told him that I can't date him anymore, he hates me. Deservedly so. I didn't even get an 'Edelweiss' on my departure.

THE ROTHBERGS

Connor is an excellent networker. He seems to befriend some very influential people and they love him for not wanting anything from them other than friendship. He's a gregarious character, sensitive and receptive. Recently he became friends with a member of the Rothberg family, South Africa's very own version of the Rockefellers. The Rothberg son, Eilat, and Connor play golf together, and we're going to Eilat's father's cocktail party.

Fancy friends don't impress me much, but I was happy to accept an invitation to accompany him to the Rothberg household – or rather, the estate spanning seven kilometres on Parktown Ridge, overlooking town. Think the local equivalent of Buckingham Palace, cognac in the library, original Matisse on the walls, chandeliers, solid-gold fittings and three-ply toilet paper, a pack of greyhounds with bejewelled collars skulking around. One did a dump on the Persian carpet, and Connor stepped in it. James Bond didn't find it amusing as he was trying to remain debonair.

The Rothbergs had just come back from watching their own horses at the races. One of them won R2,5 million in one sitting. Just a drop in the old bucket really.

PEAS: 'So which horse did you bet on, Mr Rothberg?'

MR ROTHBERG: 'I beg your pardon?'

PEAS: 'I said, which horse did you bet on? And was it a, what's the horsey word for a race again, um, trifecta?'

MR ROTHBERG: 'My horses. My own horses, my dear.'

PEAS: 'Er, but of course.'

Stupid Peas. I come from an upper-middle-class family and went to a private school. You would have thought that I was used to 'horsey' people. However, I've never been impressed by grand wealth. I'm awed by the art and the beautiful places in which these people reside, but not by money itself. I have a sneaky suspicion that Connor might've bought me here to meet his new friends because he thinks I may be impressed. They seem pleasant enough, but what do we really have in common besides Connor? I was quite happy when we made our exit.

After months of amicable cooperation, polite meetings and generally getting along, my ex-boyfriend Anthony has struck again. His mood has swung from deliriously nice to deliriously difficult. In a nutshell, he's being a complete asshole. I have no other words of appropriate description. And now, because every action has a reaction, I'm being a complete bitch. Let me explain:

We play this wonderful little game of My Stuff Your Stuff. One week we've decided who gets what. (Microwave versus TV, say.) But then it changes. He says he wants, say, the video machine. I agree to pay him an appropriate amount of money for it. He agrees to this exchange. Then in a fit of irrationality, he leaves me a voicemail message saying that he has decided he wants the video machine and that I'd better get it to him within twenty-four hours or he'll phone his lawyer. Anthony has a lawyer? Oh please, come on. Although, maybe he does? After all, he is a corporate climber. He knows those kinds of people.

This happens consistently, but each time I take the threat seriously. Then, I calm him down, we talk, we cry, I decide he's just angry with me for making us break up and then we decide again who gets what. Guaranteed, next week it'll happen again. The last argument was over the coffee cups he generously left for Giulia and me to use.

PEAS: 'What do you need a set of mugs for? You live with your parents!'

ANTHONY: 'I'll put them on the shelf in my room.'

PEAS: 'What, because they're pretty?'

ANTHONY: 'Yes. So I want them back.'

PEAS: 'Has it ever occurred to you that you're just doing this because you're angry with me and trying to make my life difficult?'

ANTHONY: 'Maybe I'll drink out of them too.'

PEAS: 'Oh come on. This is ridiculous. Fine, take the Anthony Shapiros.'

ANTHONY: 'Actually, on second thought, you can have them.'

PEAS: 'What?'

ANTHONY: 'I want the Snackwich machine.'

PEAS: 'Are you actually being serious?'

ANTHONY: 'Or one times set of Anthony Shapiros. Your choice. But one of them is coming home with me.'

I promised to make a time for him to come and collect his stuff when my parents are here, because it would be volatile and I'm scared we'll throw the kitchen sink at each other. While my step-father hates conflict, my mother and I seem to thrive on it. My mother is a fighter. Coincidentally, my father is a flighter. Fight and flight. I have a huge contradiction in my gene pool.

Anthony has now threatened to file a charge of theft for one times set of Anthony Shapiro mugs (hued in glazed mint and finished around the rim in gold gilt) despite our conversation.

Am I trapped in some sort of nightmare?

All I can do is let him take the rest of his stuff, but somehow try to reason with him about the Anthony Shapiros. How did I get into this ridiculous situation? How did we put up with each other for almost six years? This pattern of behaviour is so typical of us. I think I'm going to move to Estonia, and I'd like to take Giulia with me. Her pasta, wine and wonderful wardrobe, not to mention her invaluable friendship, simply cannot be left behind, and I could never go travelling on my own. You've got to be joking. But, don't they use lard out east? Giulia likes olive oil. This may be a problem. If there's one thing I'm learning, it's that Giulia is serious about food.

I wonder whether Connor or Bennet would ever fight with someone over Anthony Shapiro mugs. Or over who gets the George Foreman grill. Somehow, I don't think so, in fact, I don't think they'd really give a stuff. I think Connor might fight over something far more exquisite, like a piece of art. But I also believe it would be a rational argument, and if he didn't end up with the Picasso, for example, he'd walk out with the Miro instead. It makes me angry when people try to take advantage of Connor's lovely nature. He always seems to fork out if the bill is short after a large restaurant evening.

This debacle with Anthony has brought me to the conclusion that I choose intense boyfriends. Perhaps the intensity excites me, makes me more passionate, stimulates and challenges me. Or perhaps it's just the challenge? Perhaps I'd get bored with a 'normal' guy. I wonder if this pattern will continue.

I still have no idea who I really am. It's annoying. Why can't I be as self-assured and as happy in my skin as Lizzy and Giulia are? Trying to define myself might shed some light in the haze (although the haze might be a result of my new, glamorous, hard-drinking, partying lifestyle)

I tend to cause regular 'chaos' somehow. I spark chaos, am attracted to chaos and am the epitome of the word chaos itself. You'd think then, that I should be well-practiced and good at dealing with chaos. I'm not.

I am an only child who wants to find true love, so that I have a man by my side to help me conquer the world.

I am social. I always knew I was a sociable attention seeker, but now I'm really ripping the ring out of it. What's great is that I'm spending plenty of time with my favourite friends: Lizzy, Giulia, Helen, Connor and Bennet. It's always over plenty of alcoholic beverages. To some extent, we're all insufferable alcoholics trying to extract meaning from life in a hard city.

I work in publishing. And I fight with the sub-editor on an almost constant basis.

I love singing karaoke. Drunk, sober, bored, frustrated. It's loud, and if I close my eyes, I can imagine a large, booming crowd below my lit-up stage, where people fall at my feet and love me. In reality, I have a long way to go.

I own a dildo. Every girl should.

My father is eccentric. No, but seriously. I'm scared of turning into him. He flies a Cessna across the country, writes books, lives in tiny villages and has three girlfriends. We're not extremely close, although I think that has to do with the divorce and the fact that he lives in Cape Town.

My mother is into new-age healing. She has a crystal for every problem out there.

I love Johannesburg. Move over, Cape Town. I wonder whether I'll get burnt out by everything that happens here, but for now, me and the Hillbrow Tower are *toight*.

My boobs are named Hannah and Elizabeth.

My knee wart is called Yves Saint Lewart.

I can't touch egg boxes. It's a texture thing. Yet, when someone scrapes their nails over a blackboard I'm fine.

I am impatient, stubborn and self-righteous. But I'm also loyal, affectionate and gutsy. So there. I think I'm a nice person.

I am twenty-five. But I feel more like I'm eighteen at the moment.

I hate authority. Perhaps I'm meant to be president one day.

I love vodka. Helen created the Fitzy. Vodka, cola tonic and water. We all drink Fitzys now.

Some people bungee jump and sky dive. I'm scared of ferris wheels. I prefer to get my adrenaline kick elsewhere. I drive through ghettoes and townships on a regular basis. I know the back routes of Hillbrow, Yeoville and Alexandra fairly well for a white madam. It gives me inspiration and hope that not every-thing in Jo'burg is one-dimensional.

I am obsessed with architecture. My father's side of the family are all architects. I can happily wax lyrical about form following function, the Tuscan monstrosities of the northern suburbs, the grace of Herbert Baker and the raw aesthetic quality of Ponte City.

I have travelled a lot. Nothing gives me more of a buzz (besides good pot) than discovering new places. I'd like to travel overseas again soon. But only with someone. It would be too lonely by myself, I think.

I rely a lot on friends to pull me through testy times. I hope I don't rely on them too much. I just don't know where I'd turn otherwise. But, they don't seem to mind. And drinking is always more fun with friends.

CHAPTER TWO

HOW IT WORKS HERE

Giulia and I love living in Illovo. Even if our block of flats is slightly dilapidated, the suburb is an interesting one. The people living on my street consist of a cosmopolitan mix of up-and-coming black diamonds, Nigerian drug lords, corporate yuppies, retired old ladies (like Mrs Goldberg upstairs), and people like us who like to think of themselves as up-and-coming yuppies. But, really we're working-class damsels with posh tastes thanks to private-school education. It'll be me, Giulia and Mason-Rodney, my guinea-pig. (He's not quite a dog, but he's domesticated and fluffy.)

If there's one thing I can be grateful for, it's that since I left school, I insisted on being self-sufficient. And that meant living in my own place. I might've had a boyfriend to rely on most of my young age, but at least I was out of home. Giulia is experiencing out-of-home living for the first time in her life. I have no idea how that must feel.

We reside on the pretty side of Illovo – the Dunkeld side, to be exact. My flat is within walking distance of a pizzeria, a video shop, a Kung Fu Kitchen that sells dodgy, yet wholesome, meals laced with MSG, a corner café, a bottle store, the Wanderer's Cricket Stadium, a nut wholesaler, a dance studio, a key cutter and a Greek restaurant. Convenience doesn't get much better than this, especially in a city where nobody walks. If location is anything to go by, I am very fortunate.

When I first arrived in Jo'burg as an impressionable graduate refugee fresh from Cape Town three years ago, I knew nothing about this big, bad city and moved straight into a box in Fourways. I had to get into my car and drive two kilometres alongside indistinguishable Tuscan villas and car dealerships just to buy milk.

So you can imagine how happy I am now. There's something extremely rare about being able to stumble home across the road after too many ouzos with Nikos, the proprietor at Parea. I love living where I do and it has essentially made me fall in love with Jozi.

As a twenty-something living, working and playing (with an emphasis on playing) in Jo'burg, the vast city literally consumes you. One needs an outlet in downtime.

The second largest city on the African continent, following Lagos, Nigeria, Jozi is also the powerhouse of Africa where people flock from all corners of the country and the rest of the continent to attain wealth. So, life here is frenetic, fast-paced, stressful, competitive and impatient. It buzzes with an energy that refuses to sleep – quite the opposite of laid-back Cape Town where I went to university. Cape Town has a vast array of activities and physical outlets for its inhabitants. You can go to the beach, climb the mountain, visit the winelands and amble through the markets, cafés and eateries in the CBD. To people in Jo'burg, the group of people I fraternise with anyway, drink is an outlet. And now that I've been hurled out of my comfort zone, I'm learning this fast.

We work hard and we play hard. And when things are especially stressful, like when experiencing grief or a long, hard week at work, or when we simply have something to celebrate (like a Friday night), we hit a bar in the afternoon before nightclubbing. Here, we drink to de-stress. And I'm the poster girl for this at the moment. For every year that goes by in say, Graaf-Reinet, people age six months. For every year that goes by in Jo'burg people age two years.

It's not uncommon to be a heavy boozer here, especially in your

twenties. What else would you do? In a place where delayed gratification doesn't exist, and impatience and nerves run high, people
need to unwind as quickly as possible, or at least as fast as we wired
up during the week. We drink to get hopelessly drunk. This is how
it works.

As much as I love this Jo'burg-centric, irresponsible mid-twenties,
perhaps it will wear thin eventually. As Connor mentioned the other
night (over a bottle of cabernet sauvignon), 'It's not a lifestyle that's
sustainable.'

Then, of course, there's Loser's Complex. LC often comes hand in
hand with a big night out at some crazy place like the Colony or The
Manhattan Club. You drink and then do stupidly regrettable things like
phone the ex, kiss or shag someone unsavoury, drink flaming Ferraris,
spend too much money and feel like an idiot the next day. More extremely, you might prang the car, lose your wallet or wake up naked
in a friend's bed. Then, the LC is likely to manifest into something bordering on manic depression. Post-drunken blues. This pattern is something I have got to grips with, especially over the last few months.

As nuts as it is, I love Jozi. It sucks you into its vortex and you
somehow find your balance. There's no other choice. You cope. You
can't help but fall in love with its raw grit, the friendly people and
the energy. Too much holiday time in a small town drives me mental. I crave getting back to the Big Smoke after adequate time away
because I don't want to miss out. But as much as everyone is in this
together, it can be lonely if you're single.

Perhaps I'll look back on my Jozi days (when I'm retired in Aix-
en-Provence as an old lady, if I ever make it to that age) as a complete blur. Even the heady days of varsity seem less surreal. Boozing
is classed as a hobby here. In a place of extremes, and for me, a
personality of extremes, it makes sense for now. Let's pray I get
through it alive.

Something interesting has come to light. Two months since Anthony and amidst my brief arms-length dates with Hansel, apparently someone called Randy fancies the pants off me.

Randy wants to get randy with me. This has piqued the interest of the serial monogamist in me. It's been two months of loneliness. Perhaps it's time to pull myself together and look into a potential long-term male venture, surely?

I took note of this Randy at a braai that I went to over the weekend. If my judgment serves me correctly, he's a card. The joker in the pack. An amusing, sharp-tongued character with piercing blue eyes, he also strikes me as your average run-of-the mill South African guy: the kind who drinks Windhoek Lager and enjoys watching rugby. My ego needs topping up, and having this larger-than-life figure show interest in me has made me feel happy again. I juggled the evening appropriately in order to get to the party – and I knew Randy would be there. It's always easier meeting people that your friends know, after all.

I arrived there a little uncertain as to what I was actually doing there. I'd barely just dumped Hansel, and yet felt no shame at the thought of running straight into the arms of someone new. Well, potentially, anyway. I'm obviously doing better than I thought. Lizzy called me, and reminded me that I am a man-eater, which I immediately felt a little chuffed with. Me? A man-eater? A *femme fatale?* Surely there could be worse descriptions for a woman who is currently bobbing along in a sea of insecurity? However, I trust Lizzy's judgment implicitly. She knows a myriad of people, having been to three different universities, and seemingly knows everyone our age. She and Randy were at Rhodes University together and according to her, he's perfect for me. Perhaps I can still be the luckiest girl in the world – in that I won't need to go on millions of dates to find my true love. He could be right under Lizzy's discriminating nose!

LIZZY: 'If you don't like him, you can always hook up with Rob.

Although I wouldn't really recommend it, because he only really has the guts talks to girls after he's downed eight beers.'

PEAS: 'And Randy?'

LIZZY: 'Oh no, he'd have the ability to talk even if you gagged him. Just go and check him out. If all else fails, we'll have a few drinks and leave.'

If what she says is true then Randy is funny, he works in advertising (meaning he's somewhat creative, which is nice for a change), is good looking and he's interested in me. What the hell. I swung into the party, which turned out to be a Rhodes University frat house in Norwood.

There he is.

He has a small ass. A small, tight ass.

The room was full of extremely drunk people. I felt a little intimidated. Lizzy was dancing like Jim Carrey in *The Mask* (so much for small talk and slipping out quietly) and Randy seemed to be in the centre of a circle doing an embarrassingly astute rendition of *The Running Man*. I nearly left, mainly because I was about a thousand cane and cream sodas behind everyone else.

After chit chatting randomly to various acquaintances, I sat next to Randy on a paisley couch in the garden. We exchanged pleasantries while drunk people vomited around us and Lizzy took a nap at my feet. Romance was all around. It was then that I decided I kind of liked him, and he seemed quite fond of my high heels. Naturally. I always find it strange that other men could actually like me; I'm still used to only one man loving and desiring me. It's a rush – perhaps I *am* sexy after all.

At 2:00 a.m. we left. In the middle of the deserted road, he kissed me. It sounds about as romantic as a Stephen King novel, however, it was the first kiss I'd had since Anthony that made me forget where I was for a second. Hansel's kisses never did that to me. The street was empty, it was deathly quiet, with only the moon, stars and us in the middle of the road smooching. He has a really tight, little bottom, which I find delicious. We moved into my car to chat about our mutual love for *Friends*. In other words, normal post-kissing idiosyncrasies while doing a *Titanic* seventeen year olds' manoeuvre by steaming up my car, hands on glass, kissing for over two hours. I know. I'm almost embarrassed. Does anyone my age do this anymore?

We eventually went our separate ways at 4:30 a.m. and I giggled like a teenager all the way home. I like him, I do, I really do. I got randy with Randy. Okay, the joke's over. For now.

Feedback from Lizzy! He wants to see me again.

LIZZY: 'So how long did you suck on his face for?'

PEAS: 'About three hours in total.'

LIZZY: 'Ooh. I knew I was right. I'm always right. He's keen.'

This information induced coy giggling.

I heard later that apparently, some guy ran into the house after he saw us kissing on the street – real classy, Peas – and announced: 'Randy's eating Peas in the street.'

It's been almost two days and I haven't heard from him yet.

No, no, I won't panic. Why would I panic? It was just one kiss. One very long, great kiss.

I just can't stop thinking about him. If he calls me, everything will be alright. I can feel it in my waters. God, I hate this part.

PUT A FORK IN ME

Randy eventually contacted me last night, a whole three days after the party. So, in forty-eight hours, I'll be donning my favourite, lacy underwear for our date. A nervous wreck, I ironed all my clothes in my underpants. I'm excited that seeing his tiny ass in the flesh may actually come to fruition. He's taking me to Cilantro in trendy Parkhurst. I wonder if it's acceptable to order the Norwegian salmon on a first date ... It's not lobster thermidor, but it's not exactly the house lasagne either. I can't remember the last time I cared about these little things, like what to wear, what to order, what to say.

PEAS: 'Lizzy, I haven't thought about Anthony in twenty-four hours! Well, except for now, only because I bought him up.'

LIZZY: 'Who's Anthony again?'

PEAS: 'I don't know, but I can tell you that Randy has a small bottom.'

LIZZY: 'He does, doesn't he? You like?'

PEAS: 'I like.'

LIZZY: 'Now, Peas, I'm not going to be a Boring Bertha; enjoy it, but just take one date at a time. You get so *serious* about these things.'

PEAS: 'Lizzy, perhaps you're not serious enough?'

LIZZY: 'Oh please.'

Suddenly, my libido has re-emerged in full force whereas just last week I thought I'd lost it forever. I am on fire. I haven't been this attracted to someone in what seems a terribly long time. It's all very promising.

Randy and I have done most of our conversing via e-mail so far. He's a real little sweet talker. What a charmer! It's certainly working, he's managed to arouse me in my office. This alone deserves credit, since every time I have a conversation with The Sub, my sex drive shuts down for at least a week. I spent most of the day, in between researching for a piece called 'Is coriander the new basil?', partaking in a marathon e-mail flirting session. I *love* these. Pretending to work diligently whilst actually fannying about with lusty cyber talk.

From: randymcintyre@mail.com
To: peasontoast@gmail.com
Subject: hi

Hey there Miss Toast

How was the rest of the weekend?

So you keen on a spot of dinner with me on Wednesday? Let me know if you've got the time (I know how taxing deadlines can be for you journos that write about food and stuff).

By the way, you'll be glad to know that Peas 'man-eater' Toast returned a measly three results on Google. And like *You* and *heat*, Google never lies.

Luv
Randy

From: peasontoast@gmail.com
To: randymcintyre@mail.com
Re: hi

You Googled me?

From: randymcintyre@mail.com
To: peasontoast@gmail.com
Re: hi

Yes.

From: peasontoast@gmail.com
To: randymcintyre@mail.com
Re: hi

Oh dear. Please ignore the porn. I did that in my crazy youth. I don't look as good these days.

P.S. Just kidding about the porn. You didn't really find it did you?

From: randymcintyre@mail.com
To: peasontoast@gmail.com
Re: hi

If the older generation looked anything like you, I'd be spending my Friday nights at the Village of Happiness peddling G & Ts and playing strip bingo. Zimmer frame for two please. :)

From: peasontoast@gmail.com
To: randymcintyre@mail.com
Re: hi

That compliment is in a class of its own. In fact it drops the whole 'You make me want to be a better man' line into the C-grade 'Nice shoes, wanna fuck?' category. You're lovely. What kinky stuff we could get up to with our Zimmer frames ... That thought will keep me awake and horny for the rest of the day.

From: randymcintyre@mail.com
To: peasontoast@gmail.com
Re: hi

Ah, Zimmer frames, false dentures, geriatric transport aids ... Who would've thought these could have such an effect on a girl? I'm guessing that with the tangle of flesh and stainless steel, a king-size mattress might be in order.

You in a pair of stilettos (of which I know you're a fan) and nothing else is enough of a turn-on for me. Cold shower, some-one, please!

From: peasontoast@gmail.com
To: randymcintyre@mail.com
Re: hi

Would you polish my stilettos, whisper sweet nothings into my ear, feed me strawberries and cream in bed and force yourself to like Lionel Ritchie? ('Hello ... is it me you're looking for?') If you can step up to the plate, well then maybe we could sort something out.

From: randymcintyre@mail.com
To: peasontoast@gmail.com
Re: hi

Well, 'tell me how to win your heart, for I haven't got a clue.' Lionel – check!

Polish stilettos! Me and a pair of silk boxers – check!

Feed you strawberries! Fruit and Veg City (011 625 4372) – check!

Cream! God bless Clover – check!

Sweet nothings – I'm afraid I need you for that one.

From: peasontoast@gmail.com
To: randymcintyre@mail.com
Re: hi

I'll be waiting in anticipation, Lionel.

The date went extraordinarily well. I wore a skirt and heels. He wore a polyester black shirt. I've always been partial to a man in cotton, so this was an initial turn-off, but I pushed it to the back of my mind and concentrated instead on his piercingly blue eyes.

Randy is a playful character. He has a youthful, boyish energy and is possibly the funniest guy I've ever met. He's even funnier than me, which should put my nose out of joint, but every time he opens his mouth, I find myself guffawing appreciatively. Here's a person who loves the limelight as much as I do. And I don't mind moving over if it means I'm holding my corset together because he's making me guffaw with hysteria. He's different from Anthony, perhaps he's just not as serious. But as Lizzy pointed out, who wants serious anyway? I can have a non-serious serious relationship with a non-serious funny guy.

RANDY: 'You know, I'm a member of MENSA.'

PEAS (very impressed): 'Seriously?'

RANDY: 'Yip. I have an IQ of 147.'

PEAS: 'What do you do at MENSA?'

RANDY: 'Talk about intellectual stuff. You know, maths and quantum physics. It's helluva exciting.'

PEAS: 'You sure? I thought you were in advertising. Surely you'd be a full-time scientist or something if you were a member of MENSA?'

RANDY: 'Yeah, but you know, I just do advertising for the love of the game.'

PEAS: 'Oh. Hectic.'

RANDY: 'I can't back that up.'

PEAS: 'Back what up? You loving advertising?'

RANDY: 'No, that I'm a member of MENSA. I can't back any of it up. I'm having you on.'

PEAS: 'You have a strange sense of humour, Randy.'

We had moved onto Fino's for some nightcaps when I ran out of cigarettes. Stumbling (thanks to the four glasses of Morganhof) along to the petrol station to buy me some more, again we exchanged saliva like adolescents on the pavement. I couldn't handle it much longer and was dying to show him my lacy boy-shorts and see his bare bottom; I took him home with me for a cuddle, not for sex. I'm not quite ready for that yet.

I made him tea in the morning although I don't like making guys tea the next day. Mainly because the first thing I need to do when I wake up is go and wash my make-up off from the previous night in order not to look like the Bride of Frankenstein. Everything has to be perfect. Especially for a new guy. Before I went to work, he gave me a final kiss, swept the hair out of my face and whispered, 'You're gorgeous, you know that?'

Oh dear. I felt like melting into a puddle right there on the floor. And it's making me very, very excited.

Giulia seems to like him too, which is a good sign. She's usually pretty frank when she doesn't approve of some bottom-feeder I have turned my attentions to in the recent past. He promised to sample her pasta, which he said he'd heard so much about. This made her blush coyly. Randy seems to be on a winning streak with everybody.

From: connor@irishcarbomb.com
To: peasontoast@gmail.com

Have an awesome date with Ben tonight. It is Ben, isn't it?
I love you. (In that friend kind of 'oh I just love that person, don't you just love that person?' cocktail party kind of way of saying it.)
Have fun!

SORT OF KIND OF SEEING

In between a food show, of which I had to report on different ways to prepare aubergine, and almost flogging The Sub because she argued that aubergines can be used in a vegetable smoothie (um ... no), it suddenly occurred to me that I have been casually movie-seeing, dinner-eating, cuddling with and generally dating Randy for three weeks solid. I suppose he is someone I'm sort of kind of seeing now. But – living in Jo'burg, and because Lizzy insists I'm still in Man-eater Mode ('rebounding' is what Giulia calls it) – this is sure to kick start a series of untold dramas soon enough. I can just feel it brewing somehow. My current state of mind means that I'm bound to do something rash like announcing my undying love for him after two glasses of wine. I get annoyed with myself sometimes, because I seem to just *feel* too much. I'm trying to play it cool as much as I can, so I haven't introduced Randy to many people yet. Some still think I'm with Anthony, some still want me to be with Anthony and I figure I'll gradually slip Randy into my hectic social calendar as I see fit.

He is just wonderful. We've done movies, jam jars at Primi Piatti, coffees and a nap-over here and there. What I've realised about him is that he isn't the type of guy I'd normally go for at all. Surely this is a good – I must be breaking a pattern here. I've always been the Dharma and my partner the Greg. I'm usually attracted to conservative suit-wearing types in the financial or law fields, clean-cut and serious. Randy is extremely creative, probably doesn't own a suit, sticks to retro seventies apparel, is currently unemployed and searching for a job, has a wonderfully warped sense of humour and sports a sexy amount of stubble on his face. My mother is sceptical about the 'doesn't have a job' bit, but I know it's only temporary. I think he's adorable. It all feels so right! I'm not trying to replace Anthony with Randy because they're so different. Right?

RANDY: 'You're beautiful.'

PEAS: 'Ooh. Say it again, say it again.'

RANDY: 'You heard me the first time.'

PEAS: 'No, I didn't.'

RANDY: 'I have a joke ... What is blue and has sex with Catherine Zeta-Jones?'

PEAS: 'I don't know.'

RANDY: 'Me, in my little blue suit.'

PEAS: 'Right.'

I'm fast learning that Randy's jokes aren't always mature.

RANDY: 'I had to make an entire commercial once using clips from movies with a blue theme. And I made up this joke for my boss.'

PEAS: 'Did she like it?'

RANDY: 'No, she gave me a written warning and made me redo the whole thing.'

PEAS: 'Unlucky.'

RANDY: 'Well, at least I don't have to write about aubergine smoothies.'

PEAS: 'What's purple and falls out of the sky?'

RANDY: 'An aubergine joke that just crashed and burned.'

At least he challenges me; if there's one thing I get bored with quickly, its a pushover. He came over last night to watch the indie film *Garden State* with me. We didn't end up seeing much of it, mostly because I was sitting on top of him. Giulia suddenly burst into my room (luckily we had most of our clothes on) to inform us that the highly strung French-speaking family downstairs wanted to kill Randy.

GIULIA: 'Put your shirt back on, mate. They're about to kill you.'

RANDY: 'Sorry, what?'

GIULIA: 'Your car. Just run. By the way ... do you guys ever have your clothes on?'

PEAS: 'Of course we do.'

GIULIA: 'Well it seems this flat has turned into Exhibitionism Central. I'm used to seeing you waltz around naked, Peas, but Randy, I dunno, dude.'

RANDY: 'I've never walked around here naked.'

GIULIA: 'I could argue with you and I would win – simply because I am Italian and we always have the last word. Just put on your clothes and sort out your car which the Senegalese family downstairs is about to vandalise.'

Randy had unwittingly stolen a parking bay in my apartment's communal garage that belonged to an irate French-speaking family. Thank heavens I speak French because they were about to slash his tyres.

PEAS: '*Non non non, arrêtez! Je suis trés desolée!*'

IRATE FRENCH WOMAN: '*Oo az* a-parked in my le parking? Cretin, I keel eet.'

PEAS: 'No, please don't do that. *S'il vous plâit*. I like him.'

As much as adore Randy, from what I can tell, he's a bit of an island. Perhaps this is why I find him so attractive – there are so many layers to him still to be discovered. Although, sometimes I wonder whether he thinks as deeply as I do about certain things. Maybe he keeps his innermost thoughts under wraps. Perhaps his humour is a way to deflect things of real importance but once we get to know each other better, he'll open up more. Okay, we have admittedly had some serious chats, mostly about family issues and why some people drive like assholes because they don't understand clutch control, but I suspect that it will take a while to get to know the real Randy. I need to accept now that although I wear my heart on my sleeve, not everybody does. I secretly think he shouldn't be in TV advertising, but rather in radio. He's so good at impersonating people. The thought of him cutting and pasting commercials together somehow just seems like a waste of a good motor mouth.

RANDY: 'Don't you just love Dr Evil in *Austin Powers: Goldmember*?'

PEAS: 'Yeah, he's a card.'

RANDY: 'The way he puts his pinkie to the corner of his mouth and goes, "There are two things I hate in this world ... and one is nuclear warfare." And then Number Two says, "And?"

"Huh?'

"You said there were two things you hated, sir."

"Huh?"

"You said there were TWO thi ..."

"I'm sorry, huh? *Huh?* I can't hear you, huh?"

Man, it's funny.'

PEAS: 'That is funny. I think I preferred your rendition to the actual film.'

I think I prefer everything Randy does to everyone else. Is it too soon to start thinking about a future with this guy?

From: peasontoast@gmail.com
To: giuliabriattore@itye.com
Subject: plans tonight?

Dude, I haven't used my vibrator in a month! In fact, I can't even recall where it is.

From: giuliabriattore@itye.com
To: peasontoast@gmail.com
Re: plans tonight?

Damn – are you saying there's no time for you to wank, eh?!

From: peasontoast@gmail.com
To: giuliabriattore@itye.com
Re: plans tonight?

Very funny. There's ALWAYS time to wank, sistah.

From: giuliabriattore@itye.com
To: peasontoast@gmail.com
Re: plans tonight?

Okay, this me is me just being the cautious one out of us. I think Randy is a great dude, and he's made you laugh again, which is always a more pleasant person to live with, but you don't think you're getting into this too quickly? You've just come out of a six-year something – and you're practically jumping into something that could almost be as serious. I mean, you don't think you should try and be more independent this time round, Peas? If I'm speaking out of turn, I'm sorry.

Because I am very happy for you. I just don't want to see you get hurt.

From: peasontoast@gmail.com
To: giuliabriattore@itye.com
Re: plans tonight?

Giulia, Giulia, Giulia. I appreciate your advice, my friend, but I don't see where all this concern is coming from. To put your mind at ease, Randy really seems to care for me. He could be the right guy for me! Yes, he's a little strange and elusive and he's never been in a long-term relationship before, but maybe I'm the one who will change that?

Thanks for your advice, but I'm better than I've been for years!
xxx

THE RULES

I met up with Lizzy and a few others after work mainly to prove to them (and myself) that I can come up for air. And since being captured in Randy's bluer-than-blue eyes, I don't want my mates to think I'm neglecting them. The intoxicating feeling of lust can almost be completely overpowering, and if you're not careful, the rest of the world can slip past you without you even noticing. I'm going to try and be responsible with my lust and ensure that I spend adequate time with the people who have been there for me. We sat at the Jolly Roger where they offer half-price pizza and use a strong hand when pouring vodka shots.

They were just gagging for all the details of my exciting love life.

PEAS: 'Well, I've almost forgotten what you guys look like. I can't see through the haze of lust these days.'

LIZZY: 'I think I just threw up a little in my mouth.'

GIULIA: 'I must confess that you're glowing like a rock star.'

What? No. I don't 'glow'. I really don't. Maybe I'm sick.

LIZZY: 'So does this mean you're never coming clubbing again, and aren't interested in prowling for scruffy, Bohemian men on the pull?'

PEAS: 'Well, you make it sound so attractive ... Dude, hippies that don't bathe for five years have never been my thing. But I'd never turn down a proper thrash at Manhattan for a *guy*.'

GIULIA: 'Oh yeah, then where were you on Friday?'

PEAS (sheepishly): 'Watching DVDs and eating a pizza on the couch. With Randy.'

LIZZY: 'I'm starting to regret introducing the two of you. I thought I'd just got my eighteen-till-I-die mate back, and you've just slipped straight back into a relationship.'

GIULIA: 'That's it, missy. We're dragging you out this weekend. I don't care if your skin does look amazing.'

PEAS: 'Can Randy come too?'

GIULIA AND LIZZY: 'No.'

PEAS: 'All right, I'll somehow detach myself from my ball and chain and come.'

LIZZY: 'It wasn't a question. You're coming.'

GIULIA: 'And I'll be confiscating your phone for the evening. Ooh! Peas has a boyfriend.'

PEAS: 'Let's get one thing straight: I don't have a boyfriend.'

LIZZY: 'Peas has a boyfriend, Peas has a boyfriend! I'm going to vomit, but you have a boyfriend.' (Sighs.)

This conversation made me completely hot and flustered, because I do not have a 'boyfriend'. Randy hasn't said I'm his girlfriend yet, so

I don't have a boyfriend.

What defines 'having a boyfriend' anyway? According to serial-dater Connor, it's official after the third date. Although, that said, Connor is acting very strangely at the moment. I leave him messages and he only phones me back hours, sometimes even a day or two, later. It's not like him at all and I don't quite know why. Maybe he's just really busy. Meanwhile, Helen reckons it's only official after the third nap-over, all wining and dining at restaurants aside. I believe it's only official when both parties decide that it is. This can only be decided after The Talk. I haven't had The Talk with Randy. So, in conclusion, right now we're just 'seeing' each other.

And that's that.

But I am smiling a lot at the moment though, which makes for a pleasant change. When my boss asked me to ditch the article I had penned on lemon sorbet and rewrite a story on hummus in the nineties, I grinned and said, 'With pleasure.' Usually, I'd roll my eyes and go, 'I have a lot of work to do, but I'll try to squeeze it in ... somehow.' Even The Sub stopped in obvious disbelief for a nano-second while hacking apart my article with her red marker. She thinks my attitude stinks, which is ironic since she's the most emotionally volatile woman to ever have walked the planet. Somehow, at the moment, her attempt to torment me by tearing apart everything I write doesn't seem to bother me that much. I know that when I get home, Randy and I will have a good laugh about her being frigid and lonely.

I think I've put Anthony to bed – finally. I'm certain that I'm not in love with him anymore but it's still shaky ground, hooking up with someone else so quickly – two months – after a six-yearer. I do call him every now and again to see how he is and he'll usually say, 'You still seeing Randy? Why?' So as not to rub it in, I always change the topic and ask him how his mother is. Anthony will always be special to me, however, the dust finally seems to be settling, largely in part due to the miraculous appearance of Randy in my life. Things have thankfully progressed from those dark days of lying on the couch eating Pringles and watching endless episodes of *Girls of the Playboy Mansion* in tears, thinking my life had come to an end. My life didn't come to an end. In fact, I feel more alive these days than I have for years, so I don't know what everyone is going on about. Whenever someone mentions the word 'rebound', I recoil. Isn't a rebound just a convenient, casual relationship to make up for lost intimacy? What I feel for Randy is real.

The most exciting part is getting to know each other. And that takes time. I wouldn't exactly call him the most open person I have ever met but I know that there's more in there than he lets on and I can't wait until he lets it out. I just have to be patient. Not everyone is going to be vocal about how they feel, I just have to force myself to accept this. So what if the most intimate conversation we had today went like this:

PEAS: 'I think I've picked up a bug; my stomach doesn't feel so good today.'

RANDY: 'What's wrong? Did you eat something funny?'

PEAS: 'Must have. I kind of have, um, the runs.'

RANDY (squeaking): 'Girls don't pooh.'

PEAS: 'Have you ever had the runs?'

RANDY: 'What?'

PEAS: 'Seriously, just answer the question.'

RANDY: 'No. I have never ever had the runs. Ever.'

THE INTERVENTION

Lizzy and I met up for a quick coffee last night, and she ended up bringing Helen along – which ordinarily I wouldn't mind as I'd like to get to know her better but under these circumstances I was royally peeved. We ended up having an argument, right in the restaurant. I never argue with Lizzy. Well, she and I have fought once in all the years I've known her, and it was because I accused her of flirting with Anthony at a party years ago. Of course it was bollocks. We were both drunk and it ended up with us hugging each other and crying. Oh and once she told me I was being arrogant about something (and I wasn't. Okay, maybe a little, but I think she was seriously over exaggerating). We simply don't quarrel. So tonight, I was a little put out. Especially since it seemed to be Lizzy and Helen against Peas. Helen didn't need to be dragged along as well. Couldn't Lizzy have made this 'intervention' less aggressive by being just me and her?

'Peas, we like Randy, we do,' started Lizzy.

'... We're just not sure if it's wise for you to be with anyone so intensely right now,' finished Helen.

What?

'I'm getting a little sick of you two always pissing on my parade. Can't you just accept that I'm actually happy, having fun and in a healthy relationship?'

'We have to be brutally honest. We're afraid you're moving too fast.'

'Oh please! You two are being ridiculous. I have a thick skin. Thicker skins than both of you! You guys have no idea what I've been through, and not to be rude or anything, but Helen I don't even know you helluva well.'

Lizzy spoke, and Helen just nodded in agreement, puffing manically on a cigarette. Well, what else could she say, she doesn't know me that well?

'You have issues, Peas. Randy is good, perhaps for a momentary thing. I don't think he's right for you long term. And especially so soon after Anthony.'

I was about to interrupt, when Helen continued: 'I personally think it's because you need someone to take Anthony's place. Firstly, I don't really think Randy is capable of giving that to you. Secondly, he's a rebound. This is dangerous, as you're just prolonging the process of getting to grips with yourself.'

'What am I, your Psychology Masters thesis experiment? I'm *fine*. And who do you two think you are? I mean, how lucky can one girl get? I have found The One only after three tries! Well, actually two tries, because Hansel doesn't count. I am so lucky, and look at me! I'm as happy as Larry!'

They looked at me, both with arched eyebrows. Why are they giving me such a hard time?

'Okay, so he's a bit slow on the whole "you're what I've been searching for my whole life" thing. But it'll just take some patience on my part. I really don't understand why you both feel this way.'

Obviously realising how much they'd upset me, Lizzy said, 'We care for you, but we don't know if we'll be able to soften the blow when it eventually happens. And it will.'

'When what happens?'

Helen butted in, 'When he dumps you for being too needy.'

Now I was getting angry. 'Oh come on. Is this how my future bridesmaids should be talking? If you're not careful, I'll get my sister to be my bridesmaid.'

'You don't have a sister, you need sisters, and Helen is so willing. So fucking listen to us,' Lizzy raised her voice.

I was irate, ' Who are you to judge me? Why can't you just let me be happy? You could practice a bit of needy once in a while.'

'Do you realise how unhealthy that sounds, babe?' Helen said, looking downright shocked.

'You have low self-esteem,' offered Lizzy. 'You don't need a guy to make you happy, you need to be happy first.'

I went home fuming. I'm getting my life together here, aren't I? Why is it that when something good happens, people seem to get on their high horse? What do they want me to do, dump Randy and resume a life of melancholic singleness? Why would they want that?

I'm still horrendously offended. Surely they should be grateful that Randy is around, so that they don't have to deal with my so-called 'neediness' 24/7? And Lizzy did not need to drag Helen into this either! I am very angry now.

WORK BLUES

I heard stand-up comedian Chris Rock on the radio this morning:

'Every woman in this world has a woman at her place of work that she doesn't get on with. Even if she folds jeans at JC Penney for a living, she'll come home and say, "That bitch is out to destroy me!"'

Touché Chris Rock.

Unfortunately, my bad mood went with me to the office today. I just didn't have the resources to deal with The Sub. The bitch is out to destroy me.

Her focused aim is to make me look bad. And somehow she's getting away with it. I have no idea why she hates me so much. I mean, I know that there are some people that you just clash with from the outset. But this unbridled hatred? Why?

After four days of being MIA without taking leave, she waltzes in with the kind of devil-may-care attitude that makes me want to slam-dunk her head through a basketball hoop. No explanation of where she's been. No apologies. And no interrogations by the big boss as to her whereabouts.

I asked the bitch to proofread one article for me, *one article*.

'Can you look over my "Mid-West Farmhouse Breakfasts" article for me please, deadline is noon.'

'Go and fuck yourself.'

'Beg your pardon?'

'You heard me.'

'I bloody asked you nicely! I happen to have a deadline and this is your job!'

'I have to photocopy my work contract to send to the CCMA. I can't pick up everything, you know. There's only one of me, Peas.'

'And I suppose there are two of me?'

Stampeding down the warpath looking for a fight, what The Sub neglects to notice, of course, is that I am actually always busy working. I mean, I only surf the Internet on Fridays. While she phones her fiancé to break up with him, goes to the Radium Beer Hall at lunch to quaff gin and tonics, and then spends the rest of the afternoon on the phone to her mother, I am working.

Then she has the balls to tell me that she has no time to look over one article. The big boss will believe her because she's giving him head. (Ninety per cent certain anyway.)

I've been assigned to sub-edit some of her articles by Monday – because she is 'so snowed under'. Apparently I was told about this last week. I can't recall. Because if I had, I almost certainly would've called in sick. Perhaps I was in a coma. I know I smoked a lot of pot in my student days, but the conversation never happened.

I still have to do a write-up on the hamburger patty industry so I know I never said anything along the lines of: 'Well bugger it, just add on a whole pile of other crap for me to do whenever you fancy.'

And she bought herself a new Armani bag and showed Deidre the (exquisite) inner-lining in full view of my desk!

Helen and Lizzy met me for yet another emergency cuppa. I simply burst into tears at seeing them, because after my day, I didn't want my friends to fight with me too. And I suppose Helen was making an effort at being a friend to me, so I have to let it go.

'There there. Now, we like Randy and we sincerely hope it works out, but just ... try not to fall in love with him,' said Lizzy.

I appreciate that they're making an effort to try and be positive about my future (one that obviously includes Randy).

I'm introducing Randy to Connor and Bennet tonight. This could be worse than introducing him to my eccentric parents. They are the closest thing I have to brothers and will probably ask, 'So ... Colin, right? What are your intentions with our Peas?'

I'm worried about Connor; he's been acting awfully distant lately, but maybe when he meets Randy it'll cheer him up because Randy is such a funny guy. I've told Randy to practice his best jokes to win the boys over. I think a bottle of sauvignon blanc may also be in order.

From: bennet@smartjob.com
To: peasontoast@gmail.com
Subject: you getting some?

Ooh, Peas, who are you shtoinking tonight? Is it that random dude Mike???

From: peasontoast@gmail.com
To: bennet@smartjob.com
Re: you getting some?

I ain't shtoinking anyone. And his name is Randy. R.A.N.D.Y. You and Connor. I swear.

From bennet@smartjob.com
To: connor@irishcarbomb.com
Cc: peasontoast@gmail.com
Subject: Meeting Peas' new boyfriend

Peas really wants to show off her new man. Is it Dennis or Trevor? I keep on forgetting. He'd better be good enough for

our Peas. Hope he's shitting himself for the meet-the-best-guy-friends dinner.
Best you warn him, Peas.

From: bennet@smartjob.com
To: peasontoast@gmail.com
Cc: connor@irishcarbomb.com
Re: Meeting Peas' new boyfriend

Peas has a boyfriend, Peas has a boyfriend! Isn't he unemployed Peas?

From: connor@irishcarbomb.com
To: peasontoast@gmail.com
Cc: bennet@smartjob.com
Re: Meeting Peas' new boyfriend

So you do have a boyfriend! Ha ha! Peasy's got a boyfriend, Peasy's got a boyfriend! Hold on, *unemployed.* Since when were you a sugar mommy?

From: peasontoast@gmail.com
To: bennet@smartjob.com
Cc: connor@irishcarbomb.com
Re: Meeting Peas' new boyfriend

OKAY, YOU LITTLE BASTARDS. SAY THAT AGAIN. C'MON I DARE YOU. IN FACT I WANT YOU TO.
P.S. It's only short-term unemployment. So don't mention it again.

Randy was so nervous, he dropped the bottle of wine onto Bennet's driveway as we walked towards his house. Bennet, ever happy-go-lucky, calmed everyone down with a bottle of vodka.

RANDY: 'Oh dearie dearie me. Sorry about the wine mess on the old driveway, man.'

BENNET: 'Hey, it's fine, I'm sure if I get Peas a straw that the mess will be cleaned up in no time.'

PEAS: 'Very funny.'

RANDY: 'So Bennet, nice car. It's a vintage Ford Cortina 1987, is it not?'

BENNET: 'Wow ... Ronald, I'm impressed, it really is. I bought it for a steal only last year, and it just goes and goes and goes. Would you like to see under the bonnet?'

RANDY: 'It's Randy actually. Mmm. Very ... vintage, I've never seen anything quite like it.'

Charming Randy had won Bennet over just like I knew he would. Now it was just Connor.

He stared at Randy with a beady eye and arched eyebrow for most the night throughout Bennet's three courses. It was a little unnerving.

PEAS (whispering): 'Could you please make an effort here? This is my new sort-of boyfriend, Connor, for heaven's sake.'

CONNOR: 'He's holding his fork funny. Are you sure this guy is from, you know, good stock?'

PEAS: 'You're pissing me off, dude. Make an effort or else we're leaving.'

He managed to make some polite conversation from then on, and luckily with our old friend Alcohol, everybody seemed to get on well in the end.

Happiness. They love him. Hurrah! But naturally they do. There's nothing to not like. My mum and step-dad will love him too, I'm sure of it. My father is another story, but I needn't worry about that now.

Since things are going so well, I've been thinking a lot about when I plan to have sex again. And hence decided that it may be time to test out what lies under *Randy's* bonnet.

Luckily, Randy's flat is one suburb away from my office. I've decided to nip out at lunch tomorrow for a sneaky rendezvous.

As much as I love the intimacy of sex, I'm actually a prude when it comes to casual sex. I'm just not comfortable with the idea of one-night stands and am a firm believer that sex can ruin an otherwise perfect union if done too soon. As a result, I have only ever had sex with boyfriends. Luckily Randy has been incredibly understanding about this and hasn't tried to push his luck. Plus, the waiting has actually made it all the more exciting. The delicious anticipation.

Last night, after many communal drinks with Connor, Lizzy, Helen and Frances, yes, oh yes, I finally got laid.

I insisted that we have The Talk first though, if I was to be having sex with a real boyfriend.

PEAS: 'What *are* we exactly, Randy? Can you define it please?'

RANDY: 'We're Randy and Peas.'

PEAS: 'Don't get smart with me. You know what I mean.'

RANDY: 'Well, I don't want to kiss anyone else if that's what you're talking about.'

PEAS: 'Well, if we're just Randy and Peas, than why can't we kiss other people?'

RANDY: 'No, because you're my girlfriend. Are you my girlfriend? Will you be my girlfriend?'

PEAS: 'That's all I needed to know. Yes, you're my boyfriend. We're boyfriend and girlfriend.'

Almost immediately afterwards, I blurted out that it might be appropriate to engage in our first sex session.

'You sure?' he asked concernedly, but I could tell that he'd be disappointed if I suddenly changed my mind.

'Absolutely.'

Lizzy and Helen – my newfound sister, it would seem – would be proud of me for waiting this long and for getting confirmation from him. See? I'm not rushing into anything, I'm clearly going about things the right way with my head on straight. Hopefully they'll take that into consideration.

Even though our first shag was immensely enjoyable, it wasn't perhaps the most romantic sexual liaison I'd ever experienced. On the bright side, it sure beat the heck out of getting cosy in the back of a car in the KFC parking lot. We went to his place, fumbled around for condoms, and, although I was nervous, the couple of vodka tonics I'd drunk during the evening certainly helped. He was consistent, gentle and he gazed into my eyes. Thankfully, because I can't have sex with someone who doesn't make eye contact during the act. It would've been nice to have an 'I love you' before he did the deed (as Anthony would often do), but I have to be patient.

I thought it was over for the night after the first time, but we couldn't stop. If I felt like a teenager before, this has certainly opened the floodgates. We did the dirty ten times this weekend. In thirty-six hours, we had crazy monkey sex *ten times*. I feel a little bashful now, because I really wish I had held back just a little. As Giulia wasted no time in pointing out last night over pasta linguini, I have nympho issues.

'You had sex ten times in one weekend? Just like that?'

'Yeah. It's like I just couldn't get enough or something.'

'Oh my God. It's been years since I did that. You're a complete nympho.'

'Possibly. But, I haven't had sex in a while though, dude. Take that into account.'

'I don't care. I'm living with a sex maniac. Is the guy all right?'

'Shit, I hope so.'

'This is classic rebound,' she said, too matter-of-factly. 'You pomp day and night. I read it in *Cosmo* once.'

'Don't *you* start now. Perhaps we're just very sexually compatible.'

Having sex with someone numbs my mind. I'm instantaneously all his, body, heart and soul. This state of being is obviously dangerous. What if he doesn't feel the same way? After Anthony, I couldn't imagine ever sleeping with someone else again. This has happened so quickly, and now the paranoid voice at the back of my mind wonders whether Randy's just in this for the great sex.

From peasontoast@gmail.com
To: connor@irishcarbomb.com
Subject: Help. Need male advice. And fast.

Connor. I slept with Randy last night. Not that it was bad. It was great.

The problem is that I am having a full-on freak out. I usually stick to the two-month rule, right? Well I slept with him after three weeks and five days. Why didn't I hold out longer? And I'm the one who called it – I wanted to bang him like a machine! Perhaps it's because I haven't got any for a while. So now I'm going through the whole Was it too soon?/Are we doomed?/Will he lose interest?/Does he still like me?/Does he think I'm a nympho?/Do I really like him now that we've done it?/How do I do damage control?/Can I slow things down without having to ignore him for three days? etc. etc. etc.

Drink after work?

From: connor@irishcarbomb.com
To: peasontoast@gmail.com
Re: Help. Need male advice. And fast.

Classic. Can your heart beat any faster?

From: peasontoast@gmail.com
To: connor@irishcarbomb.com
Re: Help. Need male advice. And fast.

Easy, Dr Phil, you're overwhelming me with your excellent
advice. This is a CRISIS, Connor.

WHAT HAPPENED NEXT

I tend to over-analyse and obsess about everything as it is, but
this too-much-sex thing has been a real clincher. Perhaps I need to
not see Randy this week so that I don't force myself onto him all
the time. I know he likes me, at least I think so and he has called
me his girlfriend after all, but somehow I feel that banging like
rabbits might be detrimental to my trying to ease slowly into the
relationship.

I mean, maybe Lizzy was right – she obviously doesn't understand
how perfect Randy is for me – but perhaps I should cool it. I haven't
had proper time to be on my own now I'm suddenly so vulnerable. I
certainly won't confess this to them; my pride is at stake.

Time out to give Randy the much-needed break he deserves is
what's needed here. I'm pretty certain that if I don't, I'll shag him
out the door forever. I also want some more reassurance now. Verbal
reassurance at any rate. Perhaps if I hold out, he'll step forward.

I met up with my brother from another mother, The Bennet, for a
cuppa tea, followed by a stiff drink. Bennet never analyses anything
for more than three seconds, so I figured he'd be good company.

Unpredictably he didn't comment on my child-bearing hips. Bennet often comments on my foibles and I can tease him about his spare tyre or unsightly hangnail. Neither of us is ever offended. Well, there was that one time I mentioned him bumming all my cigarettes when he'd had too many drinks:

'You're being a tight-fisted meanie, buy your own cigarettes! You say you don't smoke, Bennet, but you've just had five of my smokes in one sitting!'

'Screw you, Peas, I am *not* a tight-fisted meanie.'

He subsequently sulked for two days and then took his revenge by commenting on my backside:

'Have another doughnut, Peas. It *really* looks like you need one.'

'I meet your nasty remark with complete loathing, you little prick.'

So, after that little incident we introduced a little regulatory standard, known simply as the Red Zone. He goes too far, and I say 'Red Zone'. I go too far and he'll smugly remind me about the Red Zone. Sadly, often the Red Zone is ignored until we're already in Scarlet Zone territory. But you can never hate a non-blood sibling for too long.

Bennet agrees with me about the sex thing. And he's a guy so he should know. I think it's safe to say that any sexual activity needs to be put on ice for the moment, due to the aforementioned neediness and because I'm terrified of how deeply I feel about Randy.

'I mean, just how much sex are you having, Peas?'

'Enough. I'm not sure how much Randy is used to though.'

'Oh, he'll get used to it. The neediness is another story though.'

'Yes, but ...'

EATEN ALIVE

I've somehow managed to pick up a cold, but still wanted to visit Randy last night (not for sex, but for cuddling) in the hope that when I blew my nose, I didn't look completely disgusting. It was the worst nap-over I've ever had. Not because he isn't amazing, but because his room is infested with a plague of mosquitoes. Mosquitoes love me, they'll eat me any chance they can. So in an effort to prevent this from happening, I sprayed perfume all over myself. Bad, bad mistake.

We were both devoured alive. They were *dive bombing* my face. The whole night was spent covering every inch of skin with pillow and duvet, but because it's so hot right now, I couldn't breathe, and started schvitzing unbecomingly. I was asphyxiating myself under the duvet cover.

We didn't get a stitch of sleep. Not even for two and a half seconds.

Now Randy is grumpy, because not only did he not get any sleep, but I also transferred my virus onto him.

So, exhausted, mosquito-bitten and coughing up bits of alveoli, I exited his boudoir to conquer a huge story about French cheese that I had on the cards today. Just when I need reassurance, I've distanced him more by the mosquito revolution in his bedroom, withholding sex and making him sick. Can I do anything right? He said accusingly, 'I never had mosquitoes before you slept here.' That made me really angry. That comment was completely unnecessary.

LIZZY FINDS FAME

Lizzy, unlike me, is very closed about her relationships. She never talks about them. I often wish I could be more like her, appropriately keeping some things back. Up until last night, the name of her ex-boyfriend, Gary Perkins, was spoken in whispers. They ended things years ago so he could focus on his 'singing career' without distractions like a girlfriend. Personally, I think he was just hoping he'd accumulate a svelte female groupie, but I never told Lizzy this. Gary sung in a garage band (as in, used his parents garage to record his rock ballads). One of Gary's first songs after they broke up was titled 'Drown Bitch', a song composed just for Lizzy. Since then, he's managed to secure live music venues filled with potential fans. Lizzy doesn't know what to make of it, now that the song about her is being sung in public.

'Liz, he is singing about you, you know.'

'I know. I'm not deaf.'

'Aren't you scared people are going to know it's about you?'

'Well, I'm quite flattered really. I dumped him, yet I obviously meant something to the guy. He wrote a *song* about me. That's pretty special, right?'

'It's called "Drown Bitch".'

'Yup. Luckily for me, I'm a pretty good swimmer.'

'Yeah, I suppose even if he makes you out to be the antichrist, it's because he loved you so much. That's amazing really.'

'Yeah. I just hope people don't harp on and on about it, you know? It kind of freaks me out.'

Giulia said she'd love Hendrik to write about her – even if it was called 'Your Incessant Italian-Style Nagging Drives Me Insane'. 'Think about it, people empathise. People would live vicariously through me, I'd be famous!' she said.

If I knew one of my exes had written a song about me, possibly called 'Die, Painful Journalist Woman, Die', I'd probably be flattered that he cared or felt enough to do this in the first place. But Lizzy is more private and says that although Gary always wore his heart on his sleeve, it's unnerving. I think Lizzy and Randy are of the same cloth, and that Gary and I could probably make interesting music together.

CONNOR'S BALL AND CHAIN

Connor has suddenly found himself a girlfriend. As his best mate that happens to be a woman, I am immediately suspicious. Apparently she has long, shapely legs and blonde Aryan features. That's not the problem. My problem is that he has handed me a time-share agreement. He says me and her together in the same room together will not work. I'm furious.

I'm now 'allowed' to see Connor once a week – Tuesday evenings – when Gwendolyn goes to Bikram yoga. Although I could shift my usual Tuesday DVD and cuddle night with Randy to another day, I'm so annoyed with Connor that I don't feel like doing it. And I told him so. I also made it clear that he should leave me alone for a few days so I could stew.

'You can't just allocate time to me like I'm a business acquaintance!'

'I'm just trying to do what's best for everybody, Peas. Okay, how's this for another idea … lunches during work hours and perhaps Saturdays when we all go out?'

'I'll think about it. How do you know that she and I won't hit it off?'

'I just do.'

It's like I have to sneak around and have an affair with my best friend. I don't know what Connor's bloody problem is lately.

Then, I just blew.

'Quarantine. You've put me in quarantine. And you think this is "just fine". It's an absurd load of pants that you don't even want me to meet your new girlfriend. I'm nice, aren't I? What's your problem?'

'It's not that. Of course you're nice. She's perhaps a little threatened. So I've just avoided a potential problem. Besides, you're doing a fair amount of shagging, which is keeping you out of mischief, right? I need to blow my load too. Don't worry, we'll all get together for dinner sometime.'

'You can call me when your head's screwed on properly again.'

Meanwhile, I have another challenge to deal with.

After a trying day, I dragged my wounded car home and poured
myself a stiff drink to try to sort out my frazzled nerves. Because I
had to meet The Parents.

I'm never good with these things. And it's not just with boyfriends' parents either, but anyone's parents. Lizzy and Giulia can
talk to parents about interesting, relevant topics, but as hard as I try
I seem to come off flaky and dumb. I was also invited to dinner at
Connor's parents this week – an attempt by him to make amends
for his behaviour. I momentarily forgave him and went. They are
super posh, super colonial and super scary. Granted, his mother is a
reasonable woman but I was, nonetheless, very aware of using the
correct cutlery. Coffee lords from Kenya, his parents only recently
packed it in to retire near their children in Jo'burg. They farmed at
the foot of the Ngong Hills, just like Karen Blixen. ('We had a farm
in Africa ... at the foot of the Ngong Hills ...') Gwendolyn was no-
where to be seen – but I refused to ask about her or why she hadn't
been invited. In fact, the word 'Gwendolyn' wasn't mentioned the
entire evening. It was almost like old times.

It was actually a great dress rehearsal since I figured that, com-
pared with Connor's lot, meeting Randy's parents would be quite

easy as they're apparently pretty laid back. And they were. Thank heavens. Very normal, sweet people.

Randy, however, isn't particularly normal, and stated at the table: 'Peas won't kiss me this week, Mum, because I'm growing my moustache.' Then he promptly slapped me on the ass adding, 'Peas was helluva naughty at boarding school. Tell them about the time you bunked out and almost got expelled, Peas.'

His mother was appreciatively candid, telling me over the family album that Randy was a lovely little boy, but one hell of an ugly baby.

Randy's moustache is atrocious. He's growing it like Corné's 'tache in *The Most Amazing Show* for a dress-up party. Not only does it almost take my eye out when I go near it, it looks appalling. I refuse to kiss him until it comes off. End of story. I'm making a point about this. If I can't control the way he feels about me, then a least I can try and control his facial hair.

From: peasontoast@gmail.com
To: randymcintyre@mail.com
Subject: annoyance

I've just returned from Norwood Hyper. Lunchtime grocery shopping. Don't do it: guaranteed to put you in the foulest of moods. (How many times can people bash into your trolley in forty-five minutes? Twenty-three. That's right, twenty-three times.) How was the photo shop?

From: randymcintyre@mail.com
To: peasontoast@gmail.com
Re: annoyance

I've been practicing my 'Blue Steel' expression from *Zoolander* all day for the much-anticipated trip to get my ID photos done. Unfortunately I had to deal with the manager at the photo shop. Yeah, he's thirty-five ... with long hair ... and his name's Dwayne. Doesn't that just paint a picture?

How's the rest of the day?
Xxxxxxx

From: peasontoast@gmail.com
To: randymcintyre@mail.com
Re: annoyance

My productivity at work is low. I'm trying to write about cold meats and cheese and am thinking twice about printing out the first draft because that means I actually have to get up, yes, get up off my chair to fetch the product from the printer. Horniness could save my job right now, because it hopefully means I won't fall asleep on my keyboard. I've made up a new sex position in my head. Me on mattress upside down and backwards. You on top, backwards. What do you think we should call it?

From: randymcintyre@mail.com
To: peasontoast@gmail.com
Re: annoyance

I think we should call it the Retarded Spaniel.

CHAPTER THREE

LOSING ONESELF

I am convinced that what I'm feeling are the motions of falling in love with someone. My mind is a couple of wedges short of a cheese platter. I'm anxious about this, disconcerted because, as I fall deeper, the more elusive Randy gets. But what can I do about this?

Not to say that I've never been in love before – Christ, I have – but somehow this is different. I can barely remember who I was before I met Randy. Quite a sweeping statement from a woman gone bonkers. I'm actually embarrassed.

I've certainly lost touch with reality. My head feels as if it isn't attached to my body anymore.

A whole chunk of me has been replaced by the brain-consuming forces of lust and longing. I sound as if I'm a fifteen year old who has just had her first kiss.

But, on the upside, I'm fairly sure that I'm aware of Randy's imperfections. That's why he's perfect, because these imperfections are not dark-horse complexities, insecurities or deep-rooted damage. Randy is just a laid back, happy guy who I can't help but adore. Take for example when I first introduced him to my pet guinea pig. Mason-Rodney took to him just like that, which rarely happens as Mason-Rodney is very picky.

Still, I can't help freaking out. I'm scared to death because I'm not quite sure if Randy feels the same way as me. In fact, he probably doesn't. Shit, shit, shit. I need to go out with my mates and drink myself to distraction so I can stop thinking about this.

'Lizzy, I think I've fallen for Randy.'

'This is possibly the most tragic news I've heard all week. Now I'll *never* see you. But, I can't say that I wasn't expecting this.'

'Of course you'll see me. More than ever, actually. I'm too scared to see him because of this.'

'Let's go on the jol; that should sort you out. It's always worked for me to go out and remind myself that there's actually a whole world out there.'

'But, Lizzy, what if he doesn't love me back? He sometimes acts a little distant.'

'This was exactly what I was worried about from the beginning. I won't say I told you so, but I think you're asking a little much from Randy. He is a bit immature, Peas. You're trying to get back what you lost with Anthony. You can't do that. People are different.'

'... But then what do I do?'

Again, I feel that nobody understands. Surely if someone else out there is feeling the same confusion as me, then I wouldn't feel so out of place? I'm in love. I should be happy and instead I'm freaking out.

As God presently shits on my head, I'm trying to analyse Randy's feelings. Maybe I am torturing myself for no reason. I suppose that sometimes he does act like he loves me. He brings me lunch at work sometimes and always cuddles after sex. That must count for something, right? Meanwhile, the dramas of daily life continue.

From: peasontoast@gmail.com
To: giuliabriattore@itye.com
Subject: like, what?

Dilemma. Please help.
Randy is funny and hilarious, what with walking around our

apartment willy-nilly in his doondies and all ... he is very creative and a card ... and is perfect and lovely and ... BUT he can't
cook (and I certainly can't so what the fuck is going to happen?) and he wants to call his first kid Benedict (noooooooo)
and thinks Sebastian, the name I want to call MY son, sounds
gay. Am I overreacting?

From: giuliabriattore@itye.com
To: peasontoast@gmail.com
Re: like, what?

No. Benedict is a terrible name. But if he can't cook, buy
Woolworths TV dinners. It's his walking around our flat in his
doondies that worries me.
Chill.
Baci. xx

From: elizabeth@downtoearth.com
To: peasontoast@gmail.com
Subject: shiiiiiiit

I graunched something that looks like Barney the rotund,
purple dinosaur last night.
My beer goggles don't appear to be working anymore. May I
borrow yours please?

From: peasontoast@gmail.com
To: connor@irishcarbomb.com
Subject: Randy

My dad is doing what you and Bennet do so frequently.

Forgetting the name of my new boyfriend. And it seems to be on purpose. 'Randy? RANDY? What the hell kind of a name is that?'

He used to do the same thing to my friends when I was a kid. I'll DIE of embarrassment if he does it when he meets Randy.

When he first met Anthony he went, as quick as pickled sardines are opened on the Cape Flats, 'Nice hairstyle.' I kid you not. And let's not go into what he said to John MacFarlane, that guy who liked me at school. The one with the manboobs. It's horrific to even recount. Needless to say, John never came over again. But I suppose Dad was just looking out for the O'Toast gene pool.

From: connor@irishcarbomb.com
To: peasontoast@gmail.com
Re: Randy

It's only 'cos your dad cares for you, Peas. I only forget Benjamin's name because he is still insignificant for me. Maybe once you guys get married and spawn babies I'll remember that his real name is Oliver.

From: peasontoast@gmail.com
To: connor@irishcarbomb.com
Re: Randy

How would you feel if I called Gwendolyn Caroline? Or when I actually get to MEET your new girlfriend I say, 'Hi Gloria, pleasure to meet you. Great that Connor has finally let you out of the house. Despite what he says, I actually DON'T bite.'

From: connor@irishcarbomb.com
To: peasontoast@gmail.com
Re: Randy

If you called her anything but Gwendolyn, it's my cock that
would be on the block, not yours. So don't even think about it.
Tell Trevor I'll call him by his real name, I promise.

From: elizabeth@downtoearth.com
To: peasontoast@gmail.com
Subject: Gwynnie

Dude, I met Connor's Gwendolyn last night. Well, I met her
boobs before I met her face, if we're going to be specific. They
were bulging out of her Wonderbra, desperate to erupt from
her chest. Anyway, we all ate at George's on 4th in Parkhurst
– possibly the most pretentious dinner place in this whole
province – because she wanted 'scampi'. She can't call it prawn
pasta like the rest of us. Anyway, it's an interesting union if I've
ever seen one. Have you had the pleasure of meeting her yet,
or is Connor still hiding her away from Scary Peas?

From: peasontoast@gmail.com
To: elizabeth@downtoearth.com
Re: Gwynnie

No, I haven't had the pleasure. You mean the little shit has
introduced Princess Gwendolyn to everyone except me? I'm
furious. Not that I want to be her best friend or anything. I had
to write about scampi the other day at work; gourmet seafood
is probably the only thing we have in common.

From: peasontoast@gmail.com
To: giuliabriattore@itye.com
Subject: So have you met her too?

Gwendolyn. Have you met her too?

From: giuliabraittore@itye.com
To: peasontoast@gmail.com
Re: So have you met her too?

No, but Lizzy tells me she digs scampi. I make the best scampi
in the world, so let's invite them over. If she likes scampi, she
can't be that bad.

CANE TRAIN

Mason-Rodney, my guinea pig, just upped and died last night. He
had some kind of a fit and then just keeled over.

Traumatic.

I cried and cried, phoned my ex-boyfriend and then phoned my
current boyfriend, blubbering and blowing snot bubbles. I thought
Anthony would want to know that Mason died. They were fairly
close, the two of them. I phoned Connor too, but he had to dash outside to talk really quickly because Gwendolyn was giving him uphill
about who the female voice was on the other end of the phone. So
I hung up.

Randy and I went to a cocktail party at Helen's house last night,
so naturally I drank too much cane to drown my sorrows and subsequently learned the hard way never to drink cane when you're emotional. Previously, I've only really been intoxicated on cane when I
was happy, and believe you me, it is a totally different experience.

A rundown of the evening:

Arrive at Helen's posh cocktail party. She gives us tequila at the door.

Drink cane, lots of it.

Drop bottle of cane onto pristine patio; watch it smash in slow motion into millions of fragments before a whole lot of people I don't know.

Leave the party. Randy drives my car to the Radium Beer Hall. Connor and Bennet are there. Connor is without Gwendolyn, the new, jealous girlfriend.

I become very high maintenance.

Connor thought it was extremely funny that I was being so impossibly sensitive about everything.

'So how are you, Peas?'

'What the fuck do you mean by that?'

'Was just saying hi. Jeez. Relax.'

'Oh. I'm fine.'

'You sure?'

'Yes, I am sure. I'm just peachy. *Capisce*?'

Randy showed extreme patience, especially when my boob tube fell down for all to see. He politely pulled it up, covering my bare breasts as I started crying again.

We drove to Fontana Roastery at midnight for some chicken burgers. All the while I argued adamantly with him that the road we were on was Glenhove Road, when, in fact, it wasn't. I only realised later that I was wrong – around about the same time that the chicken burger lapped up the cane in my stomach. I apologised. I can be so stubborn. We've started to banter a lot lately. Maybe it's hidden resentment and I'm trying to get some sort of reaction from the man, but if there was a honeymoon phase, it is now over.

To punish me, Randy made me buy condoms at the petrol station. This is my worst nightmare; I get so embarrassed that I just want to die. I wondered around the shop aimlessly throwing chamois leathers, chocolates, a map book and Tic Tacs into the basket and then casually approached the guy behind the counter: 'I might as well also have a pack of Midnights please.' But then I blushed and started giggling. Randy watched gleefully from the car outside.

I bought black condoms. Why? I don't know. They are so German porn flick it's frightening.

Once home, we had energetic sex and my aggressiveness was somewhat diminished.

LIKE LIKES LIKE

Randy and I are more alike than I previously thought. We egg each other on by trying to be funnier than each other and encouraging loud, clownish behaviour. For example, in public, he'll grab my poen and scream 'Cookie!' in front of a whole lot of people. Our friends sort of laugh at this, rolling their eyes, commenting, 'Oh God, here they go again.' I find the whole cookie-grabbing thing outrageously funny, whereas some people get offended: 'He's such a perve, that Randy.'

We also wake Giulia up in the mornings with our loud chatter, which she doesn't find so fantastic. I suppose we must become tiring to other people. We scream at each other – not fighty screaming but jokey squabbling. Randy will scream and then dive bomb me, we'll tussle, play a game of Let's See If I Can Hold Peas Down And Lick Her Face, I'll squeal like a banshee and so it goes.

But we do argue a lot too, especially lately. When we aren't laughing or encouraging each other to be as mad as possible, we'll fight. Mostly it's about his intimacy issues and how I feel like I'm giving him my everything and not getting the same back from him.

PEAS: 'Why do you have to turn *everything* into a joke?'

RANDY: 'I'm not. I just don't like getting all intense.'

PEAS: 'Is whispering sweet nothings into each other's

unbelievably intense?'

RANDY: 'There's a time and a place.'

PEAS: 'We're sitting on my couch in an empty flat.'

RANDY: 'And I'm watching *Anchorman*, Peas.'

PEAS: 'It's like I'm digging and digging and I'm just getting no-
where. You are completely exasperating! What do you have to
say to that?'

RANDY: 'Ron Burgundy is my hero. Check it out.'

PEAS: 'Arrrghhhggghhh.'

I feel like some part of Randy is missing in the puzzle. He's not really
giving me what I want. But is what I want too much? Is it wrong to
presume that he can be more romantic? Perhaps beneath the corny
exterior of his humour, and locked away in an impenetrable vesti-
bule, is the true Randy. But I don't have the key, and so this holy
grail of emotions is seemingly out of reach. It's driving me crazy.
I can't help comparing this relationship to my previous one, even
though I know this is not what you're meant to do. Anthony spoke
off the cuff; he professed his love for me after a month. I loved that.
He was as needy as I was. Why then, is the amazing Randy not doing the same?

It's no wonder that we fight so much with me feeling this way.
And the fights we've had so far have caught everybody's attention,
as we're not naturally discreet people. We won't scream at each
other in the middle of the road or in shopping centres, but if we happen to be surrounded by people while having a tiff, they all know
about it. It's irritating for most people involved, including us – we
just don't know how to manage ourselves.

Things we have fought about so far (usually after a few drinks):

- Sex. How I can't get enough of him and he can go happily
  without it for days.

- His complacency towards love. And how he now claims to

never have been in love before.

- Following on this, my inert fear that he'll never love me. And I secretly love him. So the fact that our love may never be mutual isn't great for me, now is it?
- His obstinate and irrational fear of messy rooms. He folds his clothes with right-angled corners. It's highly annoying because each item takes five minutes to fold. We're *always* late when Randy decides to clean his room.
- How he takes longer showers than me. Forty-five minutes in a shower is ridiculous, as far as I'm concerned. He thinks forty-five minutes in a bath is stupid.
- That he needs an entire day to himself per week – and he chooses Sunday.
- How he hates shaving when his sexy stubble gets too long and starts looking decidedly Kid Rock.

Lately, people have been commenting about our fighting. And that makes me even more insecure, because I really want to prove everyone wrong about being on the rebound.

Besides, I am hopelessly in love with him.

I don't have time, what with my insanely busy social life and laborious job, to focus on this 'self-development' that Lizzy and Helen seem to be so insistent on – and seem to believe I need to be alone in order to do it. That would mean reading a self-help book or something – way too time consuming. There are so many other fun things to be doing.

I finally got to meet Gwendolyn. When I say 'meet', I mean Randy and I bumped into the happy couple at The Corner Café and she said hello and I said hello back. It was all smiles, but the look behind her heavily eyelined eyes spoke differently. Connor was very flustered, wanting to leave as quickly as possible, shuffling his feet while making some excuse about needing to get back to his car because he'd certain he left it unlocked. He's really irritating me. And, I must say that I understand why he picked her physically – there are the huge tits – but she seems a little shallow. She was constantly checking her French manicure and barking on about needing bottled water.

I suggested Connor, Bennet and I go out for frappuccinos a few days later, because I just wanted it to feel like old times. As usual, all the women in the immediate vicinity buzzed around Connor. He continues to be the hottest property in town, especially since his two-weeker with Gwendolyn has come to an abrupt halt since yesterday. He didn't explain why, and continues to remain tight-lipped about it. Connor must make an awesome boyfriend; I must say that he's a wonderful best friend despite his annoying behaviour of late. But, why the hell does he still call Randy anything but his real name?

'Have you seen John lately?'

'No, I did, however, see Randy last night.'

'Well, has Luke found a job yet?'

Luckily at least Bennet has realised that the joke of calling Randy the wrong name has become tired.

'So how is Jeff?'

'Oh for God's sake. He's fine, Bennet. Just fine. You hate flogging a dead horse, don't you?'

'Juuuust kidding, Peas. How is Randy?'

'Thank you. He's great.'

Perhaps things will return to normal with Connor, now that Princess Gwendolyn is out of the picture.

EUGENE DOES GOOD HAIR

Giulia and I threw a party at our place on Friday night; we thought it would be a good time to bring everyone together. The last people left at 4:00 a.m., which makes us qualified super-hostesses, doesn't it?

To say that people got over-the-top drunk is a severe understatement. People were downright blotto. It was pandemonium unleashed. Everyone decided that the poster of 50 Cent on the wall was actually Chuck Norris and consequently thought he deserved to be roundhouse kicked off the wall. People were running up to said wall and kicking Chuck Cent. Then it got sleazy and the competition ended with my guests trying to shag him off the wall. It was all fun and games until I injured my knee.

Needless to say, my flat looked like Hillbrow after New Year's Eve, but Randy kindly helped me clean it up in the morning which I thought was extremely sweet.

Then, as my mother and step-dad happened to be in the neighbourhood, Randy found himself in the sudden and unfortunate position of meeting my parents. He said he was great with moms, and I was excited to introduce him to my mother, because I hoped that she'd at least see how wonderful he is.

My mother can unfortunately be an incessant nag, whereas my father has a very laissez-faire, live-and-let-live attitude. They're on opposite sides of the spectrum when it comes to parenting so it's no wonder things didn't work out between them. She is much better suited to her current husband with his fiercely German and precise way of doing things. Of course, he really warms to her 'alternative' hobbies. My mother, in short, offers alternative ethnic solutions to many of my problems.

Mum went on about how un-groomed I look. Well yes, I threw a major party last night and forgot to take off my makeup before bed, so what does she expect? Her suggestion was a capsule of evening primrose oil with witch hazel to clear up my ruddy complexion. Then she asked Randy what profession he's in. Mum doesn't like my boyfriends to be unemployed. 'You need to have your chakras rebalanced.' Randy pretended to be interested when my mother suggested his current unemployment was a result of internal distress, and his third eye chakra between his eyes (she touched his third eye, just to make a point) needed cleansing. It was almost too much to watch; Mum can be scary when she goes all new age on unsuspecting victims.

But she did laugh at Randy's silly one-liners – in between hassling me about my smoking, which delighted Randy, who hates my dirty habit no end. My mother feeds off confrontation, which only got him started too.

MUM: 'Peas, you have a new crow's foot under your eye.'

PEAS: 'No, I do not.'

RANDY: 'Well, you will get one soon. Just for the weekend's bingeing, one was due, like, yesterday.'

MUM: 'That's right, Randy. See, Peas? It's a disgusting habit, and I don't think Randy wants to see you age sooner than necessary. In fact, according to some gurus like Deepak Chopra, ageing isn't even necessary at all.'

Oh, and did I mention that my mother does yoga twice a week and consults with an ayurvedic dietician to keep her svelte body slim?

WOULD YOU ALL PLEASE SHUT UP ALREADY?

Lately I'm getting the whole give-up-smoking thing from all sides. I am given the lecture frequently, mostly by my mother, but now I'm realising that I do, in fact, have to give up because it means everyone will stop nagging me. But what scares the hell out of me is that I *will* balloon into the Michelin Man. I have quit before, and then started up again because I became fat. And gym has to be the most boring thing on this earth, and when your thighs remain the same circumference as before after sweating profusely for twenty minutes on a treadmill, one does get despondent.

I'm glad Randy met my parents though. It's another small insight into where I come from that bonds us together even more. Or am I being ridiculous?

Preparing for alone time, I took a bath and was ready to be in bed by 9:00 p.m. on Randy's time-out Sunday night, when Lizzy phoned in a state because she borrowed her new boyfriend's old phone (hers was nicked over the weekend) and she 'found' a whole lot of SMS messages from his ex. I didn't know Lizzy had been hiding a new guy behind the scenes until last night. She's such a dark horse, though. Once she dated someone for a whole three months and nobody knew about it until they broke up. So I'm not overly surprised at her suddenly having a new squeeze.

As Lizzy ranted away, something decidedly pleasant happened. I was wearing paisley men's pyjamas. This is both significant and embarrassing. In the background, I vaguely heard the doorbell ring. Suddenly, Giulia burst in, wielding a pasta colander, announcing that Randy had arrived.

Picture it. It's 9:00 p.m; I look like I've been run over by a bus with a giant zit on my cheek glistening in all its glory for all to see. In he walks in with a bunch of pink roses under his arm, smirking.

Wow. I was ecstatic. Apparently he just decided to do this on impulse on his way back from seeing his mates. It's moments like these that I imagine running off with him forever. I'd even be prepared to forego the big wedding and elope. Rebound? Hmph. Isn't he just grand?

GETTING PERSONAL

I went over to Randy's place to sleep over tonight and am still reeling from the fact that he bought me flowers on a whim yesterday. Perhaps this is a new beginning for us. Unfortunately though, my stomach isn't quite right. I was cursing myself for eating beans on toast for lunch, but still wanted to cuddle with him so went over in the hope the gas will miraculously disappear. But I am so bloated from holding everything in, I could almost take off like a hot-air balloon. I will have to hold it in for another eight hours while we sleep. Torture. I can see that tomorrow morning, I will be *most* uncomfortable.

Something perhaps not discussed very much in the beginning of a relationship is farting. One tries at the beginning to appear as perfect as possible. So, coupled with trying not to be so needy, my bathroom habits have therefore become null and void. I don't even like peeing when Randy is in my flat. When he's around, I've always sprayed on perfume in the appropriate places and I am wearing my slutty underwear. The only thing he really knows about my biorhythms is when I have my period – even then he doesn't know much, just that I get cramps.

So, what to do when you need to let one off? Leave the room? Go for a brisk walk? After six years with Anthony, we were open about these things. Am I the only one in the world that's having this disconcerting/disturbing/embarrassing problem? Of course I am.

IVY LEAGUE

Connor (still *sans* Gwendolyn), Bennet, Randy and I were invited to watch the rugby at Eilat Rothberg's last night. When Giulia heard I was going to one of the richest families in South Africa's mansion again, she asked me to bring her back some of the toilet paper because she has a strange penchant for collectables like three-ply toilet roll.

This time, less intimidated, I had a good look around. The Rothberg palace consists of twenty bedrooms, about fifteen bathrooms, eight living rooms and hall upon hall of antique furniture and paintings. And let's not forget the greyhounds walking around willy-nilly. Randy's eyes nearly popped out of his skull.

Over Bloody Marys we met a few of the younger American Rothberg cousins who had come over to South Africa to do volunteer work in impoverished communities. It was hard to imagine these Ivy League graduates, dressed in Pringle cardigans and expensive golf shirts getting their hands dirty while laying bricks and cuddling AIDS babies in stark places.

Randy then enquired about the men's room:

'Closest one is the next wing, dude.'

'Okay, how do I get there?'

'Go down the passage, turn left – no right – down the stairs, turn right, then first left into the hallway, then first left and second right, through the greyhound quarters, into the next room, ring the bell on the wall and someone will escort you there.'

On the way home, Connor said casually, 'Bye Peas. Oh, by the way I'm back with Gwendolyn.'

'Oh. Well that's great, isn't it?'

'Yip, she's a doll. '

'That's great then.'

'Gotta fly. Sex is a-calling.'

Later on Randy and I engaged in a bout of energetic sex during which we tried a new position. It didn't execute as originally planned, but it felt good anyway. I don't know whether I'm over the moon about Connor and Gwendolyn's reconciliation if it means he's going to act uncomfortably whenever I'm around.

I SPOKE TOO SOON

It's over. Again. Connor broke up with Gwendolyn three days later. This time he was more explicit about why.

'She shagged me senseless. And she had a mole on her, you know, thing.'

'I'm sorry, what?'

'Too much sex, too much mole.'

'What is with you men when it comes to women with healthy libidos? For God's sake, when did ya'll get so frigid?'

'It was more the mole.'

'On her nether region?'

'Yes.' (Squirming.)

'Oh come on.'

'It's just … distracting.'

At least I'm not the only shallow person in the village. Thankfully Randy eventually did shave off his hideous trailer-park moustache.

WELCOME TO HELL

Yesterday, I was trying to go about the business of writing about *fois gras* and sangria, when The Sub and my colleague Dierdra had a full-on cat fight right in front of my desk.

THE SUB: 'If you ask me to check the spelling on your caption one more time, I'm going to kill you.'

DIERDRA: 'Fucking do it! Or else the mistakes in this month's issue will all be your fault.'

THE SUB: 'It's lunch. I'm going shopping.'

You could have cut the tension with a knife. I pretended to type furiously and avoided eye contact. I didn't have time to get involved, still having far too much research to do. But it goes without saying that I was on Dierdra's side, of course.

However, in all honesty, it felt fantastic not to be on the receiving end of the sub-editrix, also known as Madame Votre Copy Est Crap, for a change.

I called Lizzy.

'Do you have those days where you like your career but hate your job?'

'My days mostly comprise hating my career and my job, Peas.'

'Fair enough. You're a financial analyst and would rather manage your father's farm, but in reality, sometimes you like your job, right?'

'Sure. There is one particular time I can think of. It's when my boss goes abroad for business and isn't in the office.'

'I wish The Sub would leave. But she never will. She's here to breathe down my neck for as long as I'm here and to torment me for all my sins.'

'Let's pack it in and go backpacking through Peru, Peas. I've been giving it some thought. C'mon, it would be fun, we're still too young to be tied down in the corporate world.'

'What about Randy?'

'What about Randy? He's not coming with us, that's for fucking certain. Three's a crowd.'

'I'm not sure he's the backpacking-through-Peru type anyway.'

A DATE WITH ME

I am desperate for female outings at the moment, just to get away from Randy. The more I'm with him, the more needy I become. It's like feeding the monster only makes it grow bigger.

After work, Giulia and I took a sneaky drive to the Hustler shop on sleazy Corlett Drive and bought some porn. Then, she went over to Hendrik and I had a fantastic evening alone playing with myself and watching *One Night In Paris*. Paris Hilton may be a complete airhead, but she sure knows how to put on a good show. I think I'm going to make this a weekly event. It sure helps to satisfy my off-the-charts sex drive and temporarily takes the pressure off Randy.

From: peasontoast@gmail.com
To: elizabeth@downtoearth.com
Subject: What do I buy this man?

Tick tock tick tock, three days till Valentine's Day. Fuck. What's better to get Randy: a ginormous pot plant or a shirt that he's been eyeing?
The pot plant, right? He needs one for his room. Like a palm or something.
No cards. Not going to be doing cards just yet. Or maybe I'll just write something like 'I dig it. You're cool. Peas.'
Bowling Club after work for a cheeky Bloody Mary? By the way, you've been scarce, where have you been? It's because

it's Valentine's Day, isn't it? I know you hate all this stuff. But I really need your help!

From: elizabeth@downtoearth.com
To: peasontoast@gmail.com
Re: What do I buy this man?

Bloody Mary. I need one right now. About to throw myself off a balcony I am so bored.
V-Day. Definitely not a pot plant. God, I'm glad I am single again. Tim was okay, but I hate being tied down, and at least I don't have to worry about this Hallmark crap! So much hassle. We really are on the opposite end of the spectrum to each other when it comes to this romance shit.

From: giuliabriattore@itye.com
To: peasontoast@gmail.com
Subject: cazzo

Dude. Help. I am a leeeetle panicked. *Sto' per morire!* (I'm going to die.) Meeting Hendrik's parents on Friday for the first time. Having dinner with them and ... my parents. Now we all know that I come from a large Italian family that eats five bowls of pasta in one sitting and Hendrik's parents are super-conservative Afrikaans people. We're Catholic, they're NG Kerk; we're loud and obnoxious, they're reserved. This is a recipe for disaster. How am I going to merge two opposing cultures at a dinner?

Figure I'll wear jeans and a shirt and tie my hair up all pretty, be charming and it'll go juuuust fine. What's your take on parental meetings? I mean I've never done it ... you have. *Vaffanculo.*

From: peasontoast@gmail.com
To: giuliabriattore@itye.com
Re: cazzo

Your time has come! Man, oh man oh man … can't I come too? Okay, I shall not laugh at your meeting-the-culturally-opposing-parents-in-one-sitting demise.

Don't show stomach; in fact, don't show any skin at all. That's what someone once told me and for you it's especially critical. For Randy's parents, I wore jeans, heels, a smart t-shirt thingie and tied hair up. For Anthony's folks it was grey pants and a jersey. Simple, but left all my accessories on so that they could still get a hint of the real me. An artsy-fartsy heel-loving weirdo.

Make sure there's lots of wine. I had one glass with Randy's parents; you're going to need three. Have one beforehand – it will make it less daunting and nerve-wracking. Be frank and voice your opinions. They'll like you better for it. Just be yourself. They'll love you, I know they will.

You'll be fine, *mia piccolo arancia*. We can celebrate your success over the weekend.

P.S. Oh, and pray. Over your rosary. You're gonna need it.

P.P.S. Don't mention that your daughter will be a mini Amor Vittone one day.

HEARTS A-POUNDING

It's Valentine's Day. After Anthony and I called it quits, I truly believed I'd be spending this one alone, and thank heavens I'm not. Valentine's Day is hell for those who have nobody to love them.

Randy really stepped up to the plate, and – oh dear – I've fallen in love with him all over again.

His parents are on holiday, so he spent the day slaving away over the hot stove with a recipe book in his parents' kitchen, wielding oven mitts, and, I like to think, naked, barring an apron over his miniscule derriere, learning how to cook my favourite dishes. He doesn't even know how to cook, but he bloody learnt. For me! Cripes, I felt special. Quesadillas for starters, seared Norwegian salmon for mains and chocolate something or other for pudding. The guy even phoned Giulia to get a list of my favourite French cheeses.

But first, he picked me up, rose in hand and wearing a suit (delicious), and whisked me to his parents' empty house. It was decorated with flowers, rose petals and candles. It was cheesy, but I was delighted. There were even rose petals on the bed, which we swept off before we did the deed, in case we ruined the pristine linen. I gave him a Polo shirt. A crisp white one. Lizzy helped me pick it out and Bennet gave me the approving nod. Can't see straight right now I feel so loved up.

CHAPTER FOUR

THE SPASTIC COLON

Over the weekend, we went to the Colony Arms. Randy drank cane and cream soda straight out of the jug, I dropped a drink into somebody's handbag (she didn't notice on impact of spillage), and Giulia, Lizzy and a friend of Giulia's, Diego, joined in on the festivities, some of which included dry humping the wall. Don't ask.

Let me explain the relevance of the Colony Arms. Every city has a local watering hole that you're embarrassed to admit you frequent, but that you secretly love. These places are tacky and nasty. A dive, you might even say. Establishments like this always have the same criteria: cheap booze, a house beverage, ancient-looking alcoholics that sit in the same place every day, a karaoke bar, a bugger watching rugga, and debauchery on such a monolithic scale that you wouldn't even remember vomiting on the street after a night there. And it's always a big night.

Ladies and gentlemen, I present the Colony Arms. The Spastic Colon. The 'Knee. (Situated in upmarket Craighall Park, by the way.)

The house drink is served by the jugful. Or, in more recent times, in cut-off plastic two-litre bottles. Cane and cream soda – green like a tractor, hence the name John Deere. John Deeres make people stupid – fighting, crying, uninhibited dancing, unprecedented horniness and singing the Spice Girls into a microphone on a stage.

I love singing karaoke. Drunk or sober. And it's always to something atrocious like Lionel Richie, Roxette or Peabo Bryson. Luckily my posse, especially Giulia, Lizzy, Connor and Bennet, also love singing after four John Deeres.

Diego is a witty Portuguese guy with a penchant for espetada. He wears a gold chain and is quite the little smart ass, with a mouth as sharp as a Rosettenville policeman. He's going to come and visit us at the flat sometime. I have made a new friend! See? It's possible to make new friends in dodgy drunk holes. Giulia and Diego work together and, from what I can tell, their Mediterranean roots bond them, as well as providing hours of healthy debate. They constantly argue about food, their national soccer players and European politics.

GIULIA: 'So what if our national food is pasta? People love pasta so much, you'll find pasta all over the world! Like America, South Africa, even Sweden.'

DIEGO: 'Pasta is so boring.'

GIULIA: 'I don't hear of the Scandinavians liking espetada much. Admit it, Italy is known for its food; Portugal is not.'

DIEGO: 'Italy is also known for breeding drama queen soccer players.'

GIULIA: 'Oh grow up.'

MUM'S THE WORD

Besides the loving up on Valentine's Day, and the party at the Colony, there were also more concerning events that went down over the weekend.

Much more concerning.

My mother thinks I'm a sex maniac. Let me explain. I am a sex maniac. This, I cannot deny. But there are some things in every sacred mother-daughter relationship that should just go unseen. You see, she popped in for tea on Sunday at 10:00 a.m., just about the time I got back to my own flat, still dressed in the clothes from the night before. I looked like a recently sodomised ostrich, so she wasn't charmed, to say the least. I also had John Deere all down the front of my shirt and had lost an earring.

Giulia and I had, quite absent-mindedly, left our recently acquired porn carelessly on the coffee table. It was too late; Mum saw *Horny Housewives* and *Wet Cotton Panties 2* before we could furtively remove them.

She also eyed out the condoms on my nightstand. Not ordinary condoms mind you, because that would be too easy. Rough Riders.

Surely that would be enough?

Then, as if it couldn't get any worse, she spotted my dildo. My lumo pink Bushwacker 3 000. It was gently nestling under the book I'm reading – *Belle de Jour*, prose by a London call girl. As she picked up the said book to scrutinise it, there lay my bright pink vibrator, Bushie.

Mum didn't say a word. How could she? I could barely look her in the eye. She probably went home and had an apoplexy. And I'll bet Dad got a phone call as well.

Moral: Hide your sex life away at all times. Bury it. Never let your guard down.

FARMS AND CAVES

Randy, I and a couple of other people went down to Lizzy's parents' farm for the weekend. It's always refreshing to get out of Jo'burg for a while and Lizzy's farm is the perfect place to unwind. Even super socialites like us need a break from the scene from time to time. The moment you head out of the city and all of its unhealthy, tempting offerings, one can think. This should be good, but, because we are doers not thinkers, self-reflection isn't always welcome.

Lizzy comes from outside Orkney in the Free State. A colonial haven (you drink tea with a cup and saucer), it's a beautiful Cape Dutch-style place, set amongst kilometres of maize and scatterings of stray cattle, nestling in a dwelling of old plane trees. We swam, played games, dozed on the lawn, that sort of thing.

But I was anxious much of the time. At one point I went for a walk across the farm all by myself because I was at my wits end with myself and everyone else.

Perhaps it's because today would've been my six-year anniversary with Anthony. Perhaps it's because I suddenly feel as if I need space from everyone and everything right now. Perhaps it's because Randy seemed a little off this weekend. He was kind of quiet and contemplative, when usually he's vying for centre stage with me. And there was no challenge in me being there alone. He said he just had a lot on his mind, but to me this means 'I am preoccupied with anything but you.' Maybe, like the book says, he was caving. Stupid John Grey and his *Men Are From Mars, Women Are From Venus.* His caving isn't helping anybody here, that's for sure.

I have decided to spend any spare time this week at home scrubbing the bath, vacuuming the carpets, filling the fridge with food, closing my bedroom off from the rest of the world (including Randy) and skipping parties for a while.

I don't know what is wrong with me but maybe I'll resurface a new person.

DIEGO

My vacuuming was abruptly halted because Diego, true to his promise, dropped in for a glass of wine. It's as though we've been friends forever. There's no getting-to-know-you-first small talk with this fellow, or even the slightest hint of unfamiliarity. I've clearly made an instantaneous friend here which means that at least my gregarious personality is still functioning. He flopped down on the couch, put his feet up and we watched *Desperate Housewives* together. He also helped himself to my brie in the fridge. Usually nobody is allowed to touch the Langued'oc Roussillon Brie, but I made allowances for my new friend.

Diego has also became my instantaneous armchair shrink. I

confided in him about how difficult it is sleeping next to someone as nubile and delicious as Randy, how I'm the one with the high sex drive in the relationship, not to mention the one who's in love here. I also confessed about not being able to pass wind and some other unexpected dilemmas that have come to the fore.

Diego's advice was to stop over-analysing things. He also hinted that I'm possibly deranged and shouldn't be let out in public without supervision. Feet up on the table, biting into my biltong snapsticks, he said: 'Dude, you need to stop thinking so much. Just, *sommer*, leave it.'

'If I could just leave stuff, then why would I be sitting here talking to you (while you eat my food)?'

'Chicks think too much. Analyse everything, over and over again, and what for?'

'It's not like I can help it. I wish I didn't have to over-analyse everything, but I just do.'

'You need to stop. Say, are you eating that piece of cake, or can I have it?'

'The problem with men is that they *don't think enough*.'

'Damn, this cake is top notch.'

PARANOID DREAMING

Last night I awoke crying and wailing and so did Randy – I slapped him quite hard in my sleep. He was suitably unimpressed. You see, I dreamed that he ran off with some air-headed, silicone-chested secretary from Vanderbijlpark.

Well, he's not in love with me, this I know, so perhaps this is why I dreamt this. This deep-seated fear has obviously manifested in my dreams and I'm now berating him and abusing him in my sleep. When Randy asked about the dream, pawing at his stinging face, I just told him that a pack of wolves were hunting me down before eating me alive.

Connor called earlier. He and Gwendolyn have arrived at some sort of solution concerning the poen mole. He won't say what, but they're back on. I give up caring altogether.

OBSTACLES

He did it again: 'Mosquitoes never bite me when you're not here.'

Randy, who seems to be slowly getting grumpier than I am in the mornings, blames me! Blames me because he was again bitten by mosquitoes. He ruined a perfectly good nap-over with another unfair comment. Admittedly, I am not a morning person but Randy really is the pits before 10:00 a.m.

So I bought him some new Tabbard spray and told him to shut the hell up. I broke my house arrest out of boredom and irritation with Randy, and met up with Bennet and Connor at a cocktail do. Bennet had lost the keys to his Ford Cortina again. More importantly, he let slip that Anthony is having strippers over to his place on Friday for his birthday, and that he had cracked the nod to this orgy fest. Usually this is mundane information that I wouldn't have a crisis over, but I'm feeling a little over-sensitive this week.

I forced myself to manage a small, yet casual stint of socialisation with Diego and Lizzy over a bottle of wine at our flat. Randy even made an effort to wear his insect repellent and showered me with affection.

Once everyone had left, Randy and I watched a bit of *Horny Housewives 2*, in the hope that it would send his libido soaring. This was sadly however, the worst porn I have ever seen. When porn has a panpipes soundtrack in the background right from the start, you know you're in for a cheesy ride. Not to mention the larger-than-life Romanian women with lots of, um, hair on geschmutzen everywhere.

Magically it somehow worked and Randy and I snuck off after a while to have a glorious session in my bedroom.

Diego, on my discreet request, had picked up condoms for me on the way to our flat, planning to inconspicuously hand them over. But he chose neon ones, was very obvious about the transaction and then he snacked on stuff from the fridge. He reminds me of Joey Tribbiani from *Friends*. It's comforting. Sort of.

HAIRLINE CRACKS

I thought Randy and I were back on track after yesterday's porn-viewing. But I swear to God he pulled the 'honey, I have a headache' excuse today. Before now, I was honestly under the illusion that guys wanted, or at least thought about, sex every minute of the day. Even after six years, Anthony's sex drive was still dutifully revved up. I'm not used to this.

I don't quite want to admit this, at least not to my friends, but the cracks are starting to show. It's not just about the sex. Yes, I know that he's done some super-romantic things of late, but I can't help feeling like this is all a game to him, whereas, in all likelihood, for me this is it! I'm so insecure at the moment, I must be awful to be around. By now Randy should be confessing his undying love for me and he's not. I'm antsy – I see things in black and white. And, this little grey 'I have a headache' area makes me feel extremely unattractive.

Connor tried to comfort me by saying he did the same thing to Gwendolyn yesterday with the headache story. Okay fine, but he has a valid reason: he doesn't want to see the mole again. He must not really like her that much or else he'd get over it. It'll never last.

WOMEN GET TO VOTE, BUT STILL HAVE PERIODS

Shit.

I'm completely mortified.

Yesterday was Local Election Day. I voted, naturally. That's not the excruciating part.

Randy and I had dinner at his parent's house. I wore light-coloured pants. This was a complete misjudgement – the painters are in, Aunt Rosie is visiting, I'm riding the red wave – but they were my only clean trousers. Did Randy even notice? Or was he sticking his head in the sand like he does with emotional issues? I only realised what had happened when I arrived home and undressed, and I reacted with what can only be described as yells of horror. I screamed at my pants for about a minute solid.

I don't know his parents well, which makes it even more mortifying. I'd rather that this had happened in front of the president, to be perfectly honest. I hate being a woman sometimes. Sure, I love my endless collection of stiletto heels, my blingy jewellery, my skirts, the fact that I can put on make-up, lacy underwear, push-up bras. But this? This! It's just not fair.

So, I'm chuffed about being a voter, a contributor to society, but what I'm not excited about are my pants, the parents and this mortification. I'm assuming that if Randy saw it, he would've said something. Or maybe he just couldn't. I'm not sure if I should even broach the subject with him.

Good news, then bad news straight away.

RANDY: 'So, I saw my folks again today.'

PEAS (immediate hot flush explodes onto cheeks): 'Oh, right, fantastic!' (Cringing.) 'So ... what did they say?'

RANDY: 'Why do you seem so worried?'

PEAS: 'Let's not beat around the bush. How bad was it really?'

RANDY: 'What are you talking about?'

PEAS: 'Huh? Nothing, no, no nothing.'

RANDY: 'No, what are you talking about?'

PEAS: 'I know you all know. But know that I know that you know, and I am extremely embarrassed about it.'

RANDY: 'What?'

PEAS: 'No, what? What are you talking about?'

RANDY: 'Okay ... well, they found the Valentine's Day condoms.'
PEAS: (pure solid relief) 'Oh thank you, God.'
RANDY: 'No, you don't understand. My mother is the kind of woman that thinks we don't have sex. My brother, who is married, hasn't had sex yet, as far as she's concerned.'
PEAS: 'Where'd she find them?'
RANDY: 'Next to the master bedroom spa bath.'
PEAS: 'Right.'
RANDY: 'I had to basically convince them we didn't do the dirty in their hot tub.'
PEAS: 'Right ...'
RANDY: 'Why, what were you going on about?'
PEAS: (formidable pause and squirming ensues) 'White pants. Leakage. Even told my mother who is holidaying in Mozambique about it. Mortified.'
RANDY: 'Well, I didn't see anything.'
PEAS: 'Oh. Right.'
RANDY: 'Haven't checked the dining room chair upholstery though.'
PEAS: 'Fuck.'
RANDY: 'Just kidding.'
PEAS: 'Wow. Apoplexy.'
RANDY: 'You did look good in the white pants though.'
PEAS: 'Right.'
RANDY: 'The problem is my mum thinks we're banging like rabbits. I can't face her.'
PEAS: 'My mother knows we're banging like rabbits.'

HOLY MOLEY

Men are unbelievable. Unfathomable. Yet more proof that they truly do come from another planet altogether.

Bennet smooched Gwendolyn last night. Apparently they were

both drunk and it just 'sort of happened'. Why would Bennet do that to one of his best friends? Connor is pretty pissed off, to say the least. However, what I find interesting is how they sorted it all out. Connor punched Bennet, then they had a beer, spoke about the latest golf tournament results, and not twenty-four hours later they're the best of friends again.

Now if, say, Lizzy had smooched Randy, I'd probably pull every single one of her hairs out, one by one. And never talk to her again. Not to mention chucking Randy for good. Bennet is his best friend! And yet one beer later, this situation is all in the past.

Does Connor not care? I'm secretly starting to think he may be doing what I suspect Randy is doing – biding his time until someone better comes along. Gwendolyn and Connor are, insanely, still together. He said that he's realised he needs to learn to embrace the mole. And for the rest of the evening, he and Bennet sang 'I Love Moles' to 'God Save The Queen'.

SHAVEN HAVEN

Giulia called while I was indulging in sushi at Chao Thai with Lizzy (who insisted we order off the sushi menu for health reasons and because it doesn't make one gassy) and told me to come home because she's bought wax strips and intended on de-hairing my Frodo feet.

What a mate.

Randy has vocalised his displeasure at my hairy feet. I don't want a Connor-mole situation so I've decided to let Giulia take them in hand. She may have missed her calling as a beautician; she's more at home with a waxing strip and tweezers than any girl I know.

GIULIA: 'Sit tight. Your Frodo feet will be no more after I'm through with them.'

PEAS: 'You're going to hurt me. Can't I have another glass of wine?'

GIULIA: 'No. I'll rip it off so quickly, the sting will only last thirty seconds.'

PEAS: 'But I don't even notice my fuzzy feet!'

GIULIA: 'Yeah … you might be the only person there.'

I know I can be more attractive for Randy with a little more effort – and maybe he'll love that I did something just for him. I didn't tell Giulia I was planning to let her wax my feet for Randy, otherwise she probably would've shouted at me for trying too hard.

Most guys will look directly at your boobs or ass when they first meet you. Randy looked at my feet – he has a weird foot fetish and blatantly told me when we first started seeing each other that he simply could never be with a girl with ugly feet. He couldn't see how ugly mine are because, at the time, they were stuffed into stilettos.

I have ugly feet from doing ballet. My toes have been crushed into unsightly hammer toes, and I unwittingly got hold of my mum's razor when I was four years old and shaved my feet, so I have a beautiful fuzzy ridge down the centre of them.

After weeks of trying to prevent him seeing me barefoot in broad daylight when we first got together (luckily it was winter so socks were in), he caught sight of them when I wasn't paying attention.

'You don't have the most attractive feet in the world, Peas, or should I say Frodo? But the rest of you makes up for it.'

I didn't know whether to take this as a compliment or as diplomatic innuendo for 'your feet are unbelievably ugly'.

Anyway, the waxing was painful, and Giulia and her boyfriend took glee in pulling the fuzz from my feet, but now they are smooth – dashing, in fact. I just hope Randy realises this isn't going to be a regular occurrence in my usual grooming regime, even if he did stroke them tenderly afterwards.

Meanwhile, I have decided to ignore any guilt I may feel about moving on before Anthony. During our sushi supper, Helen reiterated

how 'Anthony has been going at it hammer and tongs, pulling people left, right and centre.' It hurt. I drank lots of wine. Why this still
affects me at all is beyond me. I'm in a relationship with someone
that I adore. But I do wonder whether I gave myself enough time to
get over Anthony – even if I'm not with him anymore, I don't want
anyone else to be either.

IT'S THIS CRAZY

It appears that my ex-boyfriend Anthony has found himself a permanent squeeze to latch onto. He's shacked up with a close and
common (in all senses of the word) acquaintance of ours, Glynnis.
Believe it, because it's true. I even holidayed with the hussy once.
Her artist father sculptured Anthony and I a conch shell taken from
our Zanzibar island holiday all those years ago. Until Friday evening
it was sitting on the coffee table, but it would seem that all this matters not to Anthony.

Regrettably, I have no inclination to find out how long it's all
been going on for, but I've always been suspicious that there was
chemistry between the two of them. And now those previously paranoid suspicions have come to the fore. Lesson here: if you even
slightly think that someone is lying to you about their attraction to
someone else, then you're probably right. (Although, there is a tiny
millionth of a chance you could be wrong.)

At least Anthony never knew Randy. That much is gratifying for
the little fucker – he doesn't have to sit there in the knowledge that
perhaps Randy and I were getting it on before we split up.

The news of his girlfriend has obviously hit me like a ten-ton
train. I am very angry. As far as I'm concerned, I've been a good
ex-girlfriend. I'm dating outside of our regular friendship circle, I've
kept in touch and I've tried to protect him by trying to downplay
how serious I feel about Randy. But, he hasn't showed the same
restraint.

Luckily, I had sex four times this weekend. A carnal distraction from everything.

I like to think of myself a bit experimental in the boudoir and before meeting yours truly, Randy had never tried out my favourite position. I was beginning to worry that he was strictly a missionary man as I need to be constantly stimulated by new challenges. My favourite position basically involves a tangle of arms and legs and me sitting on top of him, and him on the edge of a hard surface. The Edgy Cock-a-Doodle-Do, if you will. It doesn't involve cranium-bending creativity – some of the best sexual positions are the most simple.

To do this week:

- Buy Jenna Jameson's autobiography, *How to Make Love Like a Porn Star*. I'm planning to leave it lying around surreptitiously so that Randy knows how important variation is to me.
- Burn Anthony's accounting textbooks that I found at the bottom of the linen cupboard.

LIVING THE ROCK STAR DREAM

... not as such.

But a good stab at it though. Friday night involved pink martinis and opulence at a Rothberg party, while Saturday involved dehydration, 45 000 people, peeing in bushes, copious quantities of tot packs, disappointment over how many commercial songs Metallica played at a mass concert ... and a whopper of a fight with Randy.

RANDY: 'If I was in an accident tomorrow and became a paraplegic, would you break up with me?'

PEAS: 'Jeeziz. I have no idea. But I'd at least try and give it my best shot. You?'

RANDY: 'It probably wouldn't last, no.'

PEAS: 'Well, fuck you very much.'

And so it went.

Conclusion: never ever talk about that kind of stuff. Especially after twenty tot packs each.

After the concert, with both of us fuming and stinky, Randy dropped me off about two kilometres from my door at 1:30 a.m.

The next day, while I looked like Frankenstein's spawn after zero sleep and had a mean hangover, he pitched up at my flat, also looking like death, to argue some more.

RANDY: 'I was only half joking about the paraplegic comment.'

PEAS: 'Why bring something like that up when we're drunk? You know it'll only end in an argument.'

RANDY: 'I thought it was an interesting thing to consider.'

PEAS: 'Why? It's not exactly a rational consideration, now is it?'

RANDY: 'Oh.'

Sometimes I question if he truly is the right person for me. Then my blinkers come on and my heart says, 'But of course he is. He's perfect in every possible way! It's just a matter of time until he wakes up and realises that I am perfect too.' I could never end it now just because he isn't meeting every single one of my high expectations. I can't help thinking that perhaps my friends were right, though. Had I been by myself for a few months after my split with Anthony, I probably wouldn't be so needy. However, I am in way too deep to back out now.

From: randymcintyre@mail.com
To: peasontoast@gmail.com
Subject: Sorry

Sorry, Popsicle, for being a prick. Best you say sorry for being a bitch now.

From: peasontoast@gmail.com

To: randymcintyre@mail.com
Re: Sorry

I'm sorry, my little schnookie poo. But remember it was your fault.

From: randymcintyre@mail.com
To: peasontoast@gmail.com
Re: Sorry

No, it wasn't. It was both of our faults.

From: peasontoast@gmail.com
To: randymcintyre@mail.com
Re: Sorry

Pants! But for the sake of taking the higher road, I'll accept your apology with grace and state mine without wincing so we can manage our conflict in a constructive manner.
X

HOUSTON, WE HAVE A PROBLEM

They're off again. Gwendolyn broke up with Connor because he refused to pay for all her cosmopolitans at Espresso in Parkhurst the other day. If their relationship isn't dysfunctional, I don't know what is. Giulia may give birth to Amor Vittone II one day but even that's nothing in comparison to these two. Although, am I one to judge? I'm starting to think my and Randy's relationship is as superficial as Connor and Gwendolyn's.

On Monday my car finally went into the panel beaters after the taxi nailed me almost two months ago. I am stuck without transport until Friday afternoon.

You can't live without a car in Jozi. It's simply not an option. So I'm forced to rely on my colleague Dierdra to give me a lift home after work, and Randy takes me in the mornings. I hate being so dependent; it frightens me.

The Sub finds my lack of motor vehicle funny. Why the need to be so cruel? Because she drives a Tata Indica and I drive a new Beetle? No. Because the boss commented on how much he enjoyed my account of red onion stew this morning. So she's pissed. Mental note: when I get my car back, I will reverse over her.

I could take a minibus taxi from Rosebank and get off in Norwood, but this is just not feasible. I used to take taxis regularly in Cape Town as a student, but they're safer and more reliable there. Also, taking a taxi would just make me angrier, since it was one of them that crashed into me, putting me in this position in the first place. I therefore do not wish to support the taxi industry at all, especially since the aforementioned taxi driver has no insurance, meaning I have to shell out R2 000 excess for my broken bumper.

I'm so sick of fighting for stuff. Fighting for my car to come back before the weekend, fighting for everything to be fixed properly, fighting to be loved or have Randy want to have sex with me, constantly being on guard because I just *know* someone is trying to rip me off. No wonder we're all ready to drown our sorrows by the weekend.

At 4:30 p.m. yesterday, I left my office, with a backpack from my overnight stay at Randy's the previous night, and walked to Norwood to wait for Giulia to pick me up. I felt like a tourist in my own town. Never before have I actually sat on Grant Avenue, sipping on coffee, waiting to be picked up. Usually I can leave whenever I like. It was cold and misty and I kept on flashing back to the time when I travelled Europe on my own. Even the waitress that usually serves me looked at me funny. And for the rest of the evening, once home, I still felt strange. I was seeing my town in a totally new light.

To rectify this feeling of weirdness, I pulled out my trusty Bushwacker 3 000 and made happy with it. Still didn't help. I was also worried that Giulia's sister, who is staying with us at the moment, could hear the electrical buzzing noise. She told me the next morning that my electric toothbrush had turned itself on in the middle of the night. I nodded sagely and said it was faulty.

ON TRYING TO EARN A SALARY

Of all the nerve ...

Gleaning and writing stories as a journalist often involves cutting through an excruciating amount of bureaucratic red tape, this I know. But today it hit breaking point.

It's not as if I write about the UN embezzling Saudi Arabian oil money to finance Kofi Annan's crack habit, or Osama Bin Laden living in a penthouse apartment on New York's 5th Avenue on US government scraps, or even the details of Brett Kebble's murder. The stuff I write about is about as exciting as watching *Bonnie's Best Buys* in a padded cell. Because I write about food and beverages, what people eat, why and how, my job is riveting. So riveting, in fact, I almost fell asleep writing that sentence. You'd think it'd be easy. It's not like I'm sitting with a dictaphone on the Western Front dodging bullets. All I have to do is wax lyrical about cuisines of the world and liaise with the head offices of large franchise chains.

Well, apparently restaurateurs are hiding the crown jewels and/or state secrets, because they are the cagiest people I've ever come across. Just try and get an interview with someone who owns a restaurant. You'd think they would jump at the free exposure. It's hard work. It's more admin dealing with franchises than with celebrity agents and I know this for certain having once written for a music magazine.

The reason I'm so annoyed is that after organising an interview with a guy who refurbished a large restaurant chain at the back-end of Roodepoort (living the rock star dream right there), he pretended not to know who I was when I arrived. And I had spoken to him on the phone just this morning, as well as three weeks ago.

So I drove all the way out there and, instead of coming back with a story, I came back with a foul temper, an empty notepad and more loser's complex that I even thought possible. Not to mention a deadline looming over my head which felt like the mothership UFO in *Independence Day*.

JERRY SPRINGER'S IN TOWN

Or just about. A classy establishment in Sandton is about to go down in flames. I wish a silent good luck to anyone in Jo'burg going to News Café.

I am entering the proverbial snake pit. And, unwittingly, so is Randy.

During Anthony's and my break up five months ago, we had to split various assets. Furniture, CDs, photographs, the lease, friends ... Well, tonight is a mutual friend's birthday party. 'Mutual' is a loaded term, as we all know that he got custody in the divorce proceedings. This is fine by me on all accounts. He's a nice enough fellow but I'm well aware that he invited me out of politeness. Perhaps he was hoping I wouldn't attend, but after the Glynnis revelation I am determined to no longer protect Anthony from meeting Randy.

So I have RSVPd for myself and Randy to attend this ridiculous drinks ensemble at which I'll be considered the bad guy simply because it's his friend's do and I'm the outsider.

Ah, then there's the ex himself. With the high probability of his new floozie with the massive milk jugs latched onto his arm.

Okay, I also want to go because it's an opportunity to walk in there looking so smoking hot that people's eyes sting. I'm going to show everyone that I am in a happy relationship. Lizzy, my trusty sidekick, promised to be on hand (just 'happening' to be at the same bar) with multiple tequila shots. But I think she's just coming along to be a fly on the wall, to be privvy to any drama that cold unfold.

I imagined endless scenarios of how it could turn out:

1) Punches are thrown between Randy and Anthony. Undoubtedly Anthony will take the first swing.

2) Punches are thrown between She with the Humungous Tits and myself. Undoubtedly I'll take the first swing, pull her hair and use foul language.

3) Anthony doesn't arrive with She with the Humungous Tits, and turns on his heels when he sees me with Randy.

4) Randy and I instantly leave if he arrives with She with the Humungous Tits.

5) His friends completely ignore me.

6) His friends fall in love with Randy, waxing lyrical about how good we are together, how funny he is, and how we should all go camping together.

7) I get hopelessly drunk, dance on the bar counter and am carried out.

8) The two other ex-partners in the group have a fight, taking the heat off our situation.

9) Anthony doesn't pitch up at all due to an untimely case of amoebic dysentery, leaving him glued to his toilet seat for the rest of the weekend.

10) Anthony doesn't arrive because his car won't start.

11) Anthony doesn't arrive because he lost track of time whilst shagging She with the Humungous Tits up against a wall, when suddenly his knob falls off, and he spends the rest of the night in ER at the Jo'burg Gen.

12) Everyone gets along famously. Anthony and Randy decide they are long-lost mates. I exit quickly.

13) We have one drink, congratulate the birthday guy and get the fuck out of there before everything dramatically explodes in a

riot of drink-throwing, hair-pulling, punching, tears and loud screaming. Then, we all get thrown out on the sidewalk.

I don't know whether to be excited or to be terrified. Or ask a mate to take pictures. I also don't know why I would put myself in this situation.

What actually happened was that we all ended up smiling really, really broadly in all of the pictures. Randy and I sat at one end of the room, Anthony on the other – and the girlfriend didn't arrive. We vaguely waved hello to each other. The evening turned out to be pleasantly uneventful, except for the time Anthony and I walked straight past each other as if we were strangers. It was significantly tame. Not even a spilled drink. I'm almost disappointed.

It made me realise that Anthony finds it hard to look at Randy and me together. Maybe I should cut the guy some slack. After all, this could be as difficult for him as it is for me. Perhaps there's still a part of him that isn't totally over me. Can it be that I'm in love with a new man, but still harbour feelings of love for someone else? Aren't break ups meant to be cut and dry? I'm so confused. My head is spinning.

CHAPTER FIVE

56 HOURS

I have given up smoking. This has to be the worst day of my life.

Christ, I am *dying* here.

I haven't seen a cigarette for exactly fifty-six hours, two minutes and fifty-four seconds. I am so uncomfortable that I'd rather be pulling out my toenails than deal with the withdrawal. It's nauseating, I feel like Renton in *Trainspotting*. Okay, it's not heroin, but I also want to rip off my skin.

From ten-a-day to nothing and what do I have to look forward to?

This:

1) Getting fat. I can't stop eating.
2) Getting stoned. Best alternative to tobacco.
3) Feeling stupid and slow as a result of getting stoned.
4) Crankiness.
5) Not being able to sleep.
6) No smoke breaks at work. In other words, no respite from the steely stares of The Sub.
7) Watching Lizzy and Helen light up willy-nilly, while I sit on my hands.

Nobody tells you about this god awful aftertaste in your mouth once you give up either. It feels like I've gargled with Domestos.

I'm so unbelievably cranky; I've even switched off my extended arm/cellphone for the day. This is big. I can't be bothered to make small talk to randoms that phone me, or even talk to Randy. So I've instead chosen to disappear.

Randy is at the pinnacle of my irritation because he gave me such a shocking speech about what happened to his great uncle because he smoked that I actually just had to give up. The choice was simply no longer mine. I have given up for Randy, not myself. And that fact in itself drives me crazy with frustration. One day I'm going to have to thank *him* for giving up, meanwhile it was me that did it. Talk about undue credit.

Fuck everybody.

And in this negative space, all I want to do is rant about Randy. We're not a usual couple. We don't have our song, I'm the only one in love, we don't kiss all day long, and I am the one who, let's face it, has the healthy libido between the two of us. Well, bugger that. More than anything, I want him to smother me with smooches. This. Irritates. Me. No. End. Why can't I be less intense? What is *wrong* with me?

All the new couples surrounding me at present can't seem to stop kissing each other, having vertical sex on the dance floor or just about, staring into each other's eyes like pavement-special puppies bonded at the hip. It's sick. But somehow I wouldn't mind having that for maybe just a week?

Gwendolyn took Connor back. Only because Bennet jokingly said he'd pay for her cosmopolitans if Connor didn't want to. I don't know why she took him back; it's anyone's guess.

TURNING OVER NEW LEAVES

I've finally ditched two habits, both lasting for as long as I can remember:

1) Frequent masturbation. My libido is dead.
2) Smoking.

The first one was easier to give up than the second.

I am trying to lift myself out of this seemingly constant state of despair brought on by losing the crutch that has endlessly helped me through crisis after crisis.

The positives:
According to my GP, if you can overcome three days you are going to be all right.

I have not smoked for three and a half days. Three days is the clincher. I am still alive. Yes, it's been pure unprecedented hell breaking the physical withdrawal, but Helen the health freak suggested I drink tons of orange juice, chew gum and devour biltong snapsticks. Helen and I have become good friends now, and not just because of Lizzy, I think. She's a real health guru – I believe if she and my mother were in a room together, sprigs of broccoli would start growing from the walls just from all the health, new-age talk going around.

'But you smoke, Helen. So there's no point telling me what to do when you're puff-puff-puffing away.'

'Ah, but I'm also eating celery sticks as I do it, my new friend.'

'Celery isn't going to cure lung cancer.'

'Do you want one or not?'

'Yes yes, fine.'

My mom says that when you discard an addiction, you go through an 'emotional detox' as well. So, all the horrid feelings that have been suppressed beneath the surface come out to play.

Randy also says I smell and taste great. In eighty-three hours of smoking abstinence, I have saved approximately R52. By the end of the month, it would account for a killer pair of leather stilettos. Possibly even from Socrati. However, inside me anger stirs like an evil beast. For with nicotine withdrawal come these unpleasant thoughts:

Pure resentment. I secretly hate Randy.

But I don't really hate Randy. I am in love with him. I've just hated him over the last three days. And because he made me give up smoking, he has to face the music. I also secretly hate him for not giving me what I want but then I hate myself for accepting less than what I deserve. I'm not fun Peas anymore. I'm miserable, snappy, unsociable Peas. I'm too depressed to even play with myself. This is serious.

Luckily, the constant taste of bleach in my mouth is slowly subsiding.

Now suppose Randy managed to get me to give up smoking, which he has done, and I turn into a psycho bitch from hell, which has happened. And suppose he then decides I'm too much admin to deal with and leaves me for another woman. I will be so mad, I will blow a gasket. I just can't win here. Unless I get him to start smoking. Then we wouldn't have this problem.

During a four-minute phone call to him, trying my best sales pitch in favour of tobacco addiction, the stubborn man refused to take up smoking as a means of easing tension, via a recreational and leisurely habit, which we can share together. He just didn't buy it, saying, 'So you wanna kill me too?' So much for that idea then.

FIERY POEN SURMOUNTS TO NOTHING

In the words of Bridget Jones: Oh my bloody God and fuck.

We all went out last night for a few drinks at the Jolly Roger. I had way too many in lieu of not being able to smoke, and all my simmering bitterness leapt out. Or so Lizzy says, because I can't remember a thing. Lizzy recounted the sorry story to me this morning:

'Peas, you were the Devil last night.'

'My head's pounding, I can't remember anything … Where is Randy? Why is he not lying next to me?'

'If I were you, I'd phone Randy the moment we get off this call and apologise.'

'What happened?' (Now I'm sobbing. Something feels very wrong.)

'Okay, here's the lowdown from the top: you started shouting at Randy accusing him of having an affair. Then you asked him why he didn't love you. On the upside, only Helen and I were present, oh, and a few of Randy's friends.'

'Fuck. Oh fuck. What have I done?'

'He drove you home, and Giulia put you to bed.'

'Do you think I still have a boyfriend? Oh my *God*. *What if I don't have a boyfriend anymore?*'

'Calm down. Just phone now and say you're sorry.'

Petrified, I took the phone in hand.

'Randy?'

'Oh, look who the cat dragged in.'

'I'm so sorry, Randy, I'm so so sorry. Lizzy just told me how I be-haved last night. Do you still want to be with me?'

' … Yeah, I guess so. But Peas, I'm embarrassed by what you said and how loudly you said it. Where do you get this stuff?'

'Randy, I'm so sorry. I'll never do it again, I don't even remember it. Please don't hate me, please!'

'I don't hate you. I just think … you've got some shit you need to sort out in your head.'

'I will, I will, I promise. Thank you for understanding!'

I was begging there. *I was begging.* If I had no power or control before, I certainly don't have any now. I feel as if I'm spiralling into a horrible little hole of self-worthlessness.

To make matters worse, my nether regions are on fire. My privates are a-burnin'. I have picked up urinary cystitis. A bladder infection. It's like peeing needles, and the problem is that you want to pee all the time. I spent a good portion of the weekend not knowing whether I had to in fact pee, or if my bladder was playing tricks with me, while wincing on the toilet. Passing razorblades is no picnic, trust me. I actually think having severe thrush would be a breeze in comparison to this. The pharmacist's recommendation did nothing for me. On Saturday, I felt as though I was squatting in a pool of hydrochloric acid. It was slightly uncomfortable, to say the least. My state of mind made it worse. I feel as if I've become a burden to everyone around me.

What I didn't need was Mum trying to analyse my infection over the phone. 'Well, Peas, it seems to me that your body is trying to give you a message.'

'And what, pray do tell, might that be?'

'That you need to perhaps respect it more as your temple instead of just a haven of delights.'

'Thanks Mum, I can always rely on you to make me feel better.'

I must somehow get control. Because I feel so goddamn awful, I've decided to take a tea-totalling sabbatical until further notice, at least until the Easter weekend. Or at least until I figure out how suddenly, after years of experienced and quasi-responsible boozing, I can turn from moderately tipsy to flat-out fudging memory lost and turn into a raging madwoman.

Meanwhile, despite my terrible bladder affliction, I'm trying to be light-hearted with Randy. You know, after the other night's debacle, not bringing up anything too intense.

For instance, I said to him in the car:

'If you had the opportunity to do anything to me ... think about it ... anything! Or you had the power to get me to do anything to you, what would it be?'

It was an innocent stab at trying to talk dirty with the guy in order to try and arouse him for later. (I picked up this useful little tip in Jenna Jameson's book.)

He replied, 'I'd want to stick it up your left nostril.'

I suppose that dirty talk is a skill, a talent. One that cannot be learnt.

At home, pressing domestic matters ensued. The drain was blocked again. Due to our apartment being about sixty years old, the pipes, drainage and general seventies puke-green design of our bathroom leaves much to be desired.

Giulia and I have tried plunging. Plunging can be fun, therapeutic, except now we're a little over it. We bought concentrated sulphuric acid drain cleaner to pour down the plug, only to strip the enamel off the bath and leave the place smelling like rotten eggs.

Then there's the actual shower. Sort of half hanging off the wall, the delightful contraption can only be used when one is standing in the bath and even then it only drips. It's an accident waiting to happen. Tonight, in a fit of frustration, Giulia stepped out of the tub, soaped down from head to toe and towelled herself down while muttering Italian profanities that would make her mum blush. She then rinsed off the remaining soap in the water from the toilet cistern.

The best thing about the day was that my poen seems to be returning to its normal equilibrium.

HE CALLS ME POPSICLE

Things seem to be getting back to normal, or at least how it was before The Drunken Rage incident. He's very forgiving, my Randy. I am relieved. We are sleeping very close to each other these days, and I absolutely love it. In the beginning, we slept on opposite sides of the bed because we couldn't sleep otherwise. Now, we lie entangled in each other's arms. He wakes me up the same way every morning: 'Okay, Popsicle, rise and shine!' Then he pulls the curtains apart to allow the streaming sun in, blinding me for three minutes.

Popsicle? Bless.

While Randy and I forge ahead in our strange little relationship, our apartment has taken a little bit of a knocking. The decrepit shower is the least of my and Giulia's problems. Since Diego (aka Joey Tribbiani or He Who Snacks Casually from Our Refrigerator) has semi-moved in with us, our place continually looks like a bomb has hit it. Diego comes around almost every second day. Mainly just to sloth about.

Last night, we decided that a dinner party was in order. I was interested to see how Connor and Gwendolyn were doing. (I like to think that Randy's and my relationship is far more functional in comparison. It's comforting.) Connor has obviously decided to bite the bullet and play happy families for a change ... in other words, he's allowing Gwendolyn and I to get together at social occasions. Diego of course would never have missed the free food.

It all went splendidly, until Diego asked Gwendolyn about the mole over the cottage pie.

DIEGO: 'This isn't a bad cottage pie, Peas ... Say, Gwendolyn, have you and Connor sorted out your issues about the mole on your poen?'

GWENDOLYN: 'I beg your pardon?'

DIEGO: 'I said, have you guys smoothed out your hang-ups over the mole on your vajayjay?'

GWENDOLYN: 'Oh my God, you didn't just ask that.'

PEAS: 'Diego. Are you mentally insane?'

GWENDOLYN: 'Oh my God, Connor, I can't believe you told Peas!'

CONNOR: 'I didn't ... well, not at first, she made me tell her why we broke up ... the first time.'

PEAS: 'Would anyone like delicious dessert?'

GWENDOLYN: 'How could you tell Diego that I have a mole on my thing?'

PEAS: 'I'm sorry, it slipped one night. It's nothing to be ashamed of, really! It's very exotic!'

CONNOR: 'Great. This is just perfect.'

DIEGO: 'Hey, it's cool; my mother has a moustache. Isn't that worse?'

GWENDOLYN: 'Take me home NOW, Connor. And NO, you're not getting any!'

CONNOR: 'Oh Jesus.'

Gwendolyn really hates me now. Apparently, she broke up with Connor for two hours, but they're back together today, so I hear. The legend of Condolyngate lives on. And although this sounds a bit selfish, it's sort of a relief to know I am not alone in my relationship struggles.

FIGHTY COUPLE

Randy and I are going away to the Pilanesburg for Easter with two other very loved-up couples. I only wish Connor and Gwynnie were coming too, as this would take the heat off us, I think. Being the obstinate, argumentative and self-righteous people that we are, we've earned the illustrious moniker of 'Fighty Couple'.

Lizzy, the truth-teller wasted no time in pointing this out to me.

LIZZY: 'Do you two ever stop fighting?'

PEAS: 'Yes, of course we do! When last did we fight in front of you?'

LIZZY: 'Yesterday. Over his nylon shirt. Remember, you said it makes him look cheap and he said you hadn't rubbed your foundation in properly.'

PEAS: 'Oh.'

LIZZY: 'Don't you just want to be single again?'

PEAS: 'No.'

LIZZY: 'You sure this rebound hasn't smoked itself out?'

PEAS: 'Stop with the *rebound* thing, Lizzy. It's actually quite hurtful when your best friend has no faith in you!'

LIZZY: 'It's not you I don't have faith in.'

PEAS: 'Talking about me and Randy is actually off limits with you then.'

LIZZY: 'Oh come on. I like to live vicariously through your rebound.'

PEAS: 'Very funny.'

Fighty Couple is a hard reputation to shake and, quite frankly, we both find this label unfair, especially in light of GwendoCon, who are always on and off. (At least we've never broken up.) No one seems to openly comment about them. It also really doesn't help in my attempts to prove to everyone how happy Randy and I actually are even if we do have our issues.

So, together we've coined a plan of action for the weekend to turn this increasingly irritating little scenario around: we're not going to be Fighty Couple anymore, even if it is the very glue that seems to keep things going between us.

We made a mental list as to how we'd do it:

- Both of us must accept that one of us will have the last word.
- On the urge to argue, we will take a deep breath and ignore the other person. This person will know he/she is being ignored for a reason and will shut up.
- If one of us needs space, that person will take the car for a drive to cool off.
- We will show each other lots of affection. Not public smooching, good Lord no, just small-time PDA.
- Under no circumstances will we be on opposing teams for games like 30 Seconds and such. (Due to us both being over-the-top competitive, we have to be on the same team so we don't fight. We both need to win. We'll win together.)
- To ease any tension, we will have sex at least once a day.

Hurrah for lovey-dovey couple that never comes up for air! Fighty Couple we are no longer! This is very exciting because it means that to some degree, Randy is trying hard to make this work, to improve our relationship. He's in it for the long haul.

If there's one thing I've learned in my trivial little existence: there's no such thing as a couple who *never* fights. Either they don't have anything to say to each other or they're lying. My mum once told me that it's dangerous when a couple never have conflict – it means that they just don't care anymore, and that they are neglecting their 'inner core demands'. So, fighting is better than no communication at all. I try to remember whenever I see one of those diabetically sweet couples that perhaps, after walking on eggshells around each other all evening, they go home and behind closed doors have a massive bust up.

These thoughts are what keep me sane when No Value Add couples (those at parties who spend the night smooching in a corner despite the crowds around them) are in my face the whole time.

FIGHTY COUPLE WINS THE BATTLE AND ZA VORRE

Well, Easter turned out well: we won the battle of not going into battle. We did this by sticking conscientiously to our rules. Randy and I never fought. Not once. In fact we got on so well that for the weekend we became one of those sugary-sweet couples that I simultaneously detest and long to be. There's hope for us! So there, Lizzy and all the other non-believers.

Now that the weekend is over, the real fun starts. My dad is coming up to see me from Cape Town this week. He is wildly eccentric, with the pomposity of Crocodile Dundee – a handful, but always entertaining. However, it is with some scepticism that I await his arrival. Dad has never been reliable. We don't talk seriously, my father and I. He's not able to concentrate on one thing for too long and cites his childhood diagnosis of ADD as the reason. I think it's because he just can't be bothered to listen. He's flying up in his newly acquired Cessna aeroplane which he bought in his retirement. I'm hoping he'll make some effort to be warm to Randy or at least not to scare him away. God forbid the word 'unemployment' comes up.

In the meantime, The Sub has taken leave for a week. This is the best news I've heard in a long time.

CONDOLYNGATE

CONNOR: 'She hates you.'

PEAS: 'Because I told Diego about the mole? C'mon! She should wear it with pride.'

CONNOR: 'Well it's a sensitive subject, Peas.'

PEAS: 'Well then tell her I have a third nipple.'

CONNOR: 'You'd be lying, and I'm trying to be honest with her.'

PEAS: 'Maybe I do have a third nipple.'

CONNOR: 'Seriously? Show me! Show me. Right now.'

PEAS: 'It's a giant mole exactly mid-way between my noombies.'

CONNOR: 'You mean ... Hannah and Elizabeth have a sister?'

PEAS: 'An unsightly sister too. But I love her. She's called Cinderella.'

CONNOR: 'Shut up.'

PEAS: 'Oh come on, you've seen me in a bikini.'

CONNOR: 'Yes, but I really need to see this thing.'

PEAS: (lifting up shirt, pushing aside bra) 'See?'

CONNOR: 'That's insane.'

PEAS: 'Now tell Gwendolyn to stop overreacting.'

CONNOR: 'Can't you send her an apology or something? She's high maintenance like that.'

Dear Gwendolyn

I'm sorry about the whole mole-on-your-nethers thing. Don't worry, I have a third nipple called Cinderella. She's probably not half as pretty as yours.

Kind regards,
Peas on Toast

Dear Peas on Toast

A third nipple? Trust *you* to have something weird like that. And you're right, the mole on my fanbelt is adorable, Connor even told me. Yours probably looks ridiculous.

Gwendolyn

Dear Gwendolyn

You are an idiot.

Peas on Toast

Dear Peas on Toast

I resent that. And I will tell Connor that you were a bitch to me.

Gwendolyn

From: peasontoast@gmail.com

To: connor@irishcarbomb.com

Subject: Your girlfriend

She's way out of line. Put a leash on her.

NEW LEVEL

Something hugely fundamental happened over the weekend that was somehow left undocumented. It's serious.

Randy and I have hit a new level of intimacy. First he let me squeeze a zit on his back. Make no mistake, I enjoyed that immensely. But then he took it one step too far, hurdling over the boundary line in one foul-smelling swoop.

He farted. Loudly. While I was sitting on his lap. He thought this was h.i.l.a.r.i.o.u.s. It *was* pretty funny. Okay, it was hilarious. Anthony would awaken me each morning with a Dutch oven. Don't ask. We almost didn't notice when one of us popped one out. I vowed this relationship would be different. So Randy and I have discussed the exchanging of noxious gases – things have changed since those few months when talking about such things was a no-go area. We decided that I'm not going to open my lunchbox in front of him, and I certainly don't want him cutting the cheese in front of me. But now that he's crossed this boundary, what's next? Soon he'll be wanting to take a dump with the door open, or scratch his balls in front of my mother.

When I later referred to the farting incident, he responded with a 'huh?' He claims not to remember it. Had I been the barbaric baffer, I'm certain this wouldn't be the case. Perhaps he's getting too comfortable around me which is instantly problematic since I'm still trying to be the perfect girlfriend around him.

MY FATHER

It is still with some trepidation that I anticipate my father's arrival in the Big Smoke next week for, in all honesty, he is one pretzel short of a snack basket. Literally. Endearingly. (Sometimes.) Mad as a hatter. An attention span rivalling that of a yak, the poster boy for Ritalin and a strange, intellectual genius.

Last year, when he retired, bought his plane, moved into a loft apartment on the Cape Peninsula, and wrote three books about anthropology, meteorology and geology, I started to believe that my father's mid-life crisis was to remain forever. My mother found happiness again after their messy divorce. I want my dad to be happy too. I do believe he deserves it, although his inability to be a normal father irks me. I've always worried since being a little girl about how my friends and boyfriends will handle his weird way of interacting with people. Randy's ultimate best personality trait is his sense of humour, so I am counting on this to soften the blow when he meets my father next week.

I have briefed Randy. No sudden movements, no wisecracks and no letting on about how often he stays over at my place. Dad may shirk many parental responsibilities, but he's still protective.

Our phone conversation yesterday epitomises our non-classic father-daughter relationship:

DAD: 'Speak.' (This is how he answers his phone.)

PEAS: 'Dad, I've been trying to get hold of you all day! Why was your phone off?'

DAD: 'Because I hate telephones.'

PEAS: 'When are you arriving? I want to prepare Giulia. The girl needs a heads up.'

DAD: 'I bought bunk beds.'

PEAS: 'Pardon?'

DAD: 'Bunk beds, you know, double storey beds.'

PEAS: (Resigned sigh.) 'Why? What the hell do you want with bunk beds?'

DAD: 'Think about it! I have four different ways to sleep! Push them together; dismantle them to make two singles, on the top, on the bottom ...'

PEAS: 'Because an ordinary double bed is just too ordinary?'

DAD: 'Now I can play with Jean-Paul (his two-year-old nephew) and hide the ladder so he's stuck on the top.'

PEAS: 'Does he enjoy being stuck on the top, Dad?'

DAD: 'No. He screams.'

PEAS: 'So it's all fun and games for you then?'

DAD: 'Correct.'

PEAS: 'When are you arriving in Jo'burg? I need to mentally prepare.'

DAD: 'Can I meet some of your friends?'

PEAS: 'If you behave.'

DAD: 'Are any of them single?'

PEAS: 'Oh my God, Dad. What did I tell you about hitting on my mates?'

DAD: 'Hey, it was only that one time. Besides, women your age don't have baggage.'

PEAS: 'Last time you hit on a work colleague of mine you frightened her!'

DAD: 'She loved it.'

PEAS: 'You're fifty-three! Dad, I'm warning you. Fine, I'll just invite all my male friends.'

DAD: 'Then I won't come. I'll go and sulk at Rosebank Mall.'

PEAS: 'How will you get there?'

DAD: 'Walk.'

PEAS: 'We've discussed this Dad. People don't walk in Jo'burg.'

DAD: 'Speaking of which, where can I park my plane?'

PEAS: 'What? At the airport?!'

DAD: 'Thing is they won't let me fly into Jo'burg International. I only have clearance to fly into Brakpan.'

PEAS: 'Sweet Darryl. I have to collect you in Brakpan? Where?'

DAD: 'The guy told me it's an airstrip next to a place called Carnival City.'

PEAS: 'Oh my shattered fat hat. *So when do you arrive?*'

DAD: 'Well that's the problem ... I've been delayed.'

PEAS: 'By what?'

DAD: 'I forgot to read the small print on my plane manual. It needs to be test flown for ten hours just outside of Cape Town for safety protocol. I don't understand why, I mean, everything looks all right.'

PEAS: 'Well best you test fly it.'

DAD: 'Who cares if a couple of bolts are loose?'

PEAS: 'You're joking, right?'

DAD: 'No. Not really.'

PEAS: 'Dad, call me once the test flying is over.'

DAD: 'I ordered a subscription of *Time* magazine. You read it?'

PEAS: 'Uh yes ... why?'

DAD: 'It's become so ... juvenile. I'll send it to you rather. I only got the subscription because they threw in a free camera.'

PEAS: 'You're a photographer by profession. You've got a camera.'

DAD: 'Ah ... but not *this* camera.'

PEAS: 'Dad, you're going to be nice to Randy, aren't you?'

DAD: 'Who is this Randy you're always speaking of?'

PEAS: (Exasperated shriek.) 'Dad!'

DAD: 'Yes yes ... sure I will.' (Evil chuckle.)

Please pass the Calmettes.

During my final year at school, my parents got divorced, after twenty odd years of marriage. It came as a big surprise to me. Helen is my only other friend with divorced parents, which is odd for this day and age. Since getting to know each other we have had long conversations about it, and how fucked up we're meant to be. Perhaps many of my issues are a result of this – but who knows, perhaps I'm just naturally riddled with hang-ups. My mum tried to get me to counselling to 'deal with the trauma of the break up' but I wasn't really interested at the time, so she planted a large rose quartz at the bottom of my bed to clear away the bad energy. Whatever.

Dad was always a firecracker – flying planes over scary terrain, like the Drakensberg, and cracking strange jokes in front of my friends. But, he was also the strict one. God help me if I was late for my curfew or if I talked back to him. The wooden spoon and I go way back; all he had to do was look at it when I was kid, and I knew my bottom was about to be tanned.

Mum was the stable one, and who I could talk to about everything. Now she's gone a bit off the wall with all her new-age stuff, but she's still there for me when I need her.

As an only child, people automatically assume you're a spoiled brat. Granted, I did get to do a lot of things that other kids didn't. My parents took me on holidays overseas, I had piano lessons, I boarded at a private school. But that's where it ended. My parents believed that experiences would shape me, not things. And they were right. We didn't have a television in our house until I was twelve and even then I was only allowed to watch for an hour a day.

I had a happy childhood. I missed having a brother and sister, but I had lots of friends and they were always allowed over. I consider myself lucky. So I guess I mustn't be too damaged. Dad had a happy childhood too. And still is, so it would seem.

CHAPTER SIX

HOW TO TICK ME OFF

On Friday we went to a house party. The host was a sultry Spanish siren who was so tactile that for a brief time I thought she was hitting on Randy and me simultaneously. She squeezed my bum and told me I was gorgeous and then turned her attention to Randy, her boobs all but pressed into his chest.

'Do you mind if I steal him away for five minutes to chat?' she whispered huskily in my ear.

I was really stuck. We'd arrived late and there were only a few smatterings of drunkard plebeians around her unfamiliar house, and I had no one to talk to. To reply 'No, I'm afraid you cannot steal him away,' would make me look like a jealous, insecure girlfriend. To ask 'Why?' would make me seem like a jealous, insecure girlfriend. This was a no-win situation so I could only surrender and smile, letting him go with the touchy-feely Spanish seductress. I went and sat on the loo for ten minutes and read a three-year-old *Marie Claire*. Still struggling with the feeling that Randy may walk out of my life at any second, this scenario was utterly excruciating. It was horrible; I felt very Bridget Jones on a fat day.

Returning from the bathroom, I sat next to Randy, visibly seething because I felt as if I was intruding on their conversation. She even had the nerve to suggest that I talk to her boyfriend to amuse myself. He was sitting unconscious and drooling elaborately on the floor. I'd rather have chatted to the imposing statue of Frida Kahlo by the door – at least her eyes were open.

Out of sheer desperation, I made some excuse about feeling sick and went for a clonky, angry walk down the lonely and deserted street of suburban Parkview, wondering whether any of my guy friends would ever have the nerve to ask Randy to step aside so that they could chew the fat with me privately. Especially if he knew nobody at the party. Highly doubtful. Women can really be the pits. Even when Connor and Gwendolyn are together, I make a concerted effort not to be too pally-pally with him. It's just basic respect. Even though she and I share a mutual contempt for each other, I'm not a wanton boyfriend-borrower.

When we eventually left the party, I didn't say goodbye to the Spanish tart. Randy was ever apologetic for her lack of manners but not before commenting on the herpes blister growing on my lip. As if I didn't notice it there already.

Women love Randy. They really love him. Randy has a large bunch of female friends – which is okay, since I hang around with a lot of men myself. He oozes charm, is sensitive, can be an absolute riot, is a good shoulder to cry on and has a lovely smile. So, understandably, women are constantly around and I've become used to it. I deal, but what I will never get used to is royal blatant rudeness.

Be a good-looking woman, ask me if you can spend five minutes with my boyfriend alone, and leave me at a house party where I don't know a single soul. But you're not really asking me, you're telling me. And actually you're just telling me to get lost so that you can lure my boyfriend in with your stupid sultry eyes.

OUCH

I did something stupid yesterday. I called up Anthony, who is leaving to go to Europe for three months, to meet and touch base before he left. You see, I still miss our conversations.

We met at JB's in Melrose Arch I asked him almost straight away, well, immediately after I offered to share my cheesy nachos with him:

'So, have you and Boobs slept together?'

'Yes.'

'Do you love her?'

'Yes.'

It felt like a bullet hurtling through my chest. You know you should never ask, but you still don't expect a blatant answer even though you know it's a possibility. Hearing it for real is awful. Someone has finally usurped me. And how is it that he gets the happy ending and I don't? Randy hasn't told me he loves me, and it's starting to really tick me off. Am I not worthy of love? Am I not worthy of *anything*?

'I'm not sure I'm ready to hear about your new sexual liaison. This was a bad idea.'

'Fine. I don't know why you had to ask. Goodbye then. Have a nice life.'

He stormed off.

Our meeting lasted no more than forty-five seconds. I took the rest of the cheesy nachos home in a doggy bag for Diego.

I barely made it to my car before starting to sob. I wailed all the way home. I sobbed in the garage. I sobbed on the stairs leading to my flat. I sobbed in my flat, on the couch, on my bed, in the kitchen. I cried for two hours solid.

It wasn't really necessary to tell Randy I'd met up with Anthony. Besides, it had lasted less than a minute. He regularly meets up with his legion of ex-girlfriends, this I know, but we never discuss it.

My imagination is torturing me. The image of Anthony and She with the Humungous Tits banging up a storm rattled around in my head the whole night, and each time it popped up, whilst watching *Nip/Tuck* with Lizzy and Diego or when I took a bath, I had to physically stop myself from having a panic attack. It's a small miracle I didn't give in to a cigarette with Lizzy and Diego. If there ever was a time to start up again it was after this taxing little obstacle.

During my crying staccato and conscious control in foiling the urge to vomit, I realised two shocking truths that have recently come to the fore:

Anthony no longer loves me.

Randy will never love me. I really am a random girlfriend.

God it's depressing. Anthony may have just been the only person on this earth to ever love me. And now he loves someone else. Someone with sizeable knockers, something I do not have.

One thing I am looking forward to is spending five boozy days at Bennet's house at the Vaal River with all my friends and Randy. Bennet's family has a cottage on the banks of the river, about an hour's drive south of Jo'burg. This is where Jo'burgers go for a quick but sufficient weekend away – it's not far, is *trés* convenient, and Bennet's hospitality ensures that we get regular Vaal intervals during hectic work periods in the city.

Please may I be sufficiently distracted from the Anthony debacle. And may I anaesthetise myself with gin and tonics, good company and lazy boat rides.

MINI-BREAK AWAY FROM THE CITY

Well, the five fleeting days on the Vaal River were nothing short of fabulous, thank goodness. Bennet outdid himself as host – he didn't even lose his keys or burn the lasagne – a first. And Gwendolyn and Connor only broke up twice the whole time. Lizzy brought beef fillet from her farm, and ran around with a bottle of Apple Sourz in order to keep everyone merry and mellow.

Peas' fail proof recipe for a good weekend away
Fill the days with boozy afternoon lazing in the sun, boat rides and competitive card games. Randy won seventeen games of poker in a row. In retrospect we should've strapped him to a chair at Emerald Casino and made him our little money-making machine.

Take the piss. My group of mates talk the biggest load of shit all the time. Randy did the poen-grabbing 'Cookie!' thing constantly, and everyone just accepted his strange behaviour and him as one of our own.

Make sure someone gets lost on the way to the destination, simply for story value. On the way there while Connor and Gwendolyn argued on the back seat about her waxing procedure and how it resulted in her mole swelling up, Lizzy got lost. When they finally made it, we went to a dodgy, ravey nightclub together in WherethefuckVereeniging, which involved trance music, a dark room and plenty of neophyte-type people. Some had three eyes, I swear it.

Surround yourself with members of the opposite sex. Need I elaborate? Lizzy and I were surrounded by boys the entire weekend. Seventeen boys to be precise. Pure heaven, as I happen to prefer male company at the best of times. Not only are they less admin and have less hang-ups, boys are cards. Connor, as usual, stripped off all his apparel in the middle of dinner and recited a poem, complete with dramatisation, for our benefit. Even after a thousand beers, he was admittedly very articulate.

Run out of petrol at night on the boat when drunk, just for shits. We went for a long boat ride to Stonehaven, a pub on the banks of the river about ten kilometres upstream one night, and ran out of petrol. Bennet and Randy rowed to the nearest house using water skis (Bennet had lost the oars) with us singing 'Michael Row the Boat Ashore' (really loudly) for morale. Only to arrive on the banks in front of a house and interrupt a wedding.

Fires. The kind in a fireplace. When you're freezing your ovaries off, sit in front of one and drink red wine. (It works with cane and coke as well if you're out of the classy stuff.)

Have a sinful amount of sex. Randy and I did.

Find a new favourite word that everyone uses all the time. 'Poen' has become an official word in our circle. Its usage has become mainstream among us. Pun/poen/ poon: (n) short for punani. Calling someone a 'vagina' is no insult – but rather a term of endearment, so Gwendolyn should've been happy when Connor called her his 'little poen'. But she wasn't.

MY FATHER'S ARRIVAL

Crisis. My life is about to turn upside down as it always does when Daddy moves in.

'You get to meet the big guy tonight, you lucky little bugger,' I told Randy.

This is how it played out:

Dad runs in from Trabella Pizzeria across the road, where he was busy drinking gin and tonics with his date who is an architect – a lady half his age – to meet Randy before we head off for dinner.

DAD: 'Randy, right? Nice to see you again!'

RANDY: 'Uh … we've never met. But nevertheless … a pleasure.'

DAD: 'Where're you taking Peas tonight?'

RANDY: 'The Spur. They're having a R25 rib special.' (Dad thinks this is the funniest thing he's heard all his life and starts laughing uproariously.)

PEAS: 'You'd better be joking.'

DAD: 'Randy, are you coming for a flight in my aeroplane on Saturday?'

RANDY: (Gulp.) 'I guess so.'

DAD: 'Peas, why don't you want to meet my architect date?'

Me: 'Because we're on the way out the door.'

DAD: 'She's a little … big, sure. But come on! You're interested in architecture, aren't you? She could be a good contact for you.'

PEAS: 'Dad, a fat architect isn't going to help me in my shitty food-magazine job. Trust me.'

DAD: 'Maybe she can help you design a building?'

(At this stage, Randy is looking more than perplexed and doesn't quite know what to say or do.)

PEAS: 'Because I want to design a building?'

DAD: 'Well ... it's an option.'

PEAS: 'An option for what? I'm staying over at Randy's place to-night, Dad, so don't wait up okay?'

DAD: 'Please use protection.'

Dear God, he said that. Right in front of the poor guy.

Then, in the car on the way to the fancy Singing Fig in Norwood:

PEAS: 'I guess now you know what I mean by loopy.'

RANDY: (Formidable pause.) 'He's a little psycho.' (Last word is a high-pitched shriek.) 'No, I actually think he's cool. Nuts, but cool.'

Dinner was lovely. I ate Norwegian salmon, he had Cajun chicken linguini.

Later, we did the dirty on a Louis XV chair at his place. I have to admit, he's good like that, bringing out the fancy furniture if I ask for it.

I got an e-mail recently from an old flame that I dated after school who I still keep in contact with.

From: alansmithkins@global.com
To: peasontoast@gmail.com
Subject: My new wheels

Hiya Peasypoo
It's been a while hasn't it? When was the last time we spoke? You're probably still with that guy, whatshisname ... Andrew? Or was it Anthony? So you're getting married soon, I suppose. I can just see you now: getting ready to make babies.
The best memory I have of you is vomiting on my shoes during

my Matric Farewell, after we snuck in three bottles of wine to get the party going. What a legend. Oh well, nothing new my side, except I moved out of home. I was living in the Tsitsikamma forest for a while in a wigwam to experience the hippie lifestyle. It was okay, 'cept it's not really me. Anyway, I bought a business – a laundromat, Wishy Washy Launderers. Geddit? And a new car, you'll love this: a flaming red Audi A3 Turbo with bucket seats and a conversion system.

Keep it real,

Al

A new Audi A3 turbo. In flaming red. Let's forget the baby-making comment for a second. The man owns what is possibly the best vehicle in the world. Please understand that I'm a chick who loves cars. I don't talk about them constantly like men do, but I can stand back and admire the German craftsmanship of a vehicle like any car fanatic. Perhaps I was meant to be a boy? My dad certainly hoped so. Cars, and fast cars at that, turn me on more than Brad Jolie-Pitt. (He's so three years ago anyway.)

Anthony's A3 is gold. If there's any injustice in the world, it's that *both* my ex's own the car that I lust after. Like how a Brakpan housewife lusts after a velour Morkels sofa set. Or how a gold digger lusts after a Rothsberg. This, for those with quantitative retardation, is a lot of lust.

I'm a woman of simple tastes. All I need in this world, in a material sense, is an Audi A3 Turbo and heels from Socrati. Even if it means living in a box on the side of the William Nicol highway because I'm paying off the car and the exquisitely handcrafted Italian spike-heel uppers, I'd be one happy high-maintenance bitch.

Bastards.

I was wondering why Connor had been so quiet of late and he finally admitted that Gwendolyn had broken up with him. This time for an entire week.

PEAS: 'Why?'

CONNOR: 'We had an argument. Nothing serious. It's all better now.'

PEAS: 'What did you fight about?'

CONNOR: 'Nothing, nothing serious. Say, Peas, do my feet smell?'

PEAS: 'I've never physically smelt your feet, dude. And from my standpoint, I don't think so.'

CONNOR: 'I knew it! I'm phoning her right now.'

PEAS: 'She broke up with you because you have smelly feet?'

CONNOR: 'I'll phone you back. I'm going to tell her that you think I don't have stinky feet.'

PEAS: 'No wait, I think that's a mista ...' (Phone goes dead.)

From: gwendolyn.oreary@imaprincess.com
To: peasontoast@gmail.com
Subject: Mind your own beeswax

Peas

Where do you get off telling Connor you think his feet smell like a bunch of daffodils? He says you told him you love his feet, when actually, Peas, THEY SMELL LIKE BOVINE MANURE. So stop having him on, and thanks to you, he won't use his new Scholl Foot Scrub.

From: peasontoast@gmail.com
To: gwendolyn.oreary@iamaprincess.com
Re: Mind your own beeswax

~~Dearest Gwendolyn~~
~~Fuck off.~~

~~From Peas~~

Dear Gwendolyn

I am happy for you. No truly, I am happy that you and Connor have reached such an intimate place in your relationship. I do not give a continental fuck if his feet smell. I don't know how I got involved in this in the first place.

P.S. The Body Shop makes a great brand of foot-odour diminisher, maybe he'd prefer that?

From: peasontoast@gmail.com
To: giuliabriattore@itye.com
Subject: I just saw Amor Vittone

Just saw Amor Vittone at Rosebank Mall. She was wearing espadrilles with clam diggers. When you and Hendrick incubate a half Itye-half Afrikaans child, please ensure that I am its godmother so that this fashion faux pas never happens to it.

From: peasontoast@gmail.com
To: elizabeth@downtoearth.com
Subject: (none)

Hi dude
So the day has been wonderful. I mean besides rewriting a feature on hazelnut praline, Connor and Gwendolyn have decided to get me involved in their kinky foot-fetish thing.
Thank fuck Randy and I are a pretty normal couple. I think.

All is not well.

Randy has tonsillitis. The world has come to an end.

But seriously. Men all turn into babies when they're sick – this is a universally accepted trait.

Make no mistake, I love babying my boyfriends when they're ill. I'll wipe the fever from their forehead, feed them chicken soup and get them antibiotics. But my caring nature is short-lived. Three days later, I'm bored with the whole whining, pitiful performance.

In first year varsity, when Anthony and I were living in res, he contracted glandular fever. I offered to walk to town and buy him stuff. Only, after walking there and back in the hot sun, I realised I'd forgotten the juice he'd asked for.

'What? You forgot ... *the juice*? Well,' he croaked, with a pained expression, and then in an exaggerated whisper, he heaved, 'I'll ... just ... have ... to ... get ... it ... myself,' all the while attempting to lift himself off the bed melodramatically, only to flop down again. 'I can't. I'm just too ... weak.'

I ended up having to walk down to the shops again.

Randy holds his own as well. He's perhaps even a touch more demanding when it comes to the physical affection. As in 'Stroke my hair' or 'Can I nestle my (weary) head in your bosom?' And when I ask him if he's feeling any better (he's been on antibiotics for three days for chrissakes) I get: 'No. Not at all.'

'Not even slightly better?'

'No. I think I'm actually getting worse. I have a cough now.'

'You sure?'

'I think ... I might be dying.'

Oh. My. God.

Although, I confess that I do enjoy stroking his hair.

TUNA AND BAPTISTS

Diego came round to smoke pot and watch the religion channel on DStv on Friday, as he's become accustomed to doing. Is it that he just loves our company or that his satellite TV has been disconnected? He insists that evangelical southern Americans screaming the praises of God is hilarious but I'm not so sure. I think he's secretly Baptist. I wonder whether the neighbours find the soothing sounds of God endearing.

We got so horrifically goofed, I'm surprised I can actually remember this. Admittedly, the religion channel is hysterical when you don't know what's, erm, potting. We watched a fascinating excerpt on why the world is going to end in 2019 and if, by that time, we're not saved by Jesus, we'll be going straight to the burning fires of hell. This was philosophised by a decidedly orange man from Alabama in a hound's-tooth suit.

People do the most creative things when they're stoned. Take Connor. Once at varsity, after baking and devouring a dozen of those space cake things, he tried to fax a girl's ass to New Zealand. But creativity came, in this case, hand in hand with stupidity. He presumed that if she just sat on the fax machine, and we punched in a random international dialling code an imprint of her ass would be miraculously transported to some person's desk in downtown Auckland.

Usually when people get the munchies, they snack on biscuits, leftovers in the fridge, chocolate and cheese. Then there's that small portion of the population that'll opt for uncooked penne, seeds or Nesquik straight out of the tin. Like us.

On Friday I was game to consume anything, hell even the rabbit pellets (we have those?) at the back of the cupboard looked appetising. But I, for some reason, craved tuna. So while Giulia cooked up a pomodoro pasta surprise, I snacked on tuna out of the can. Then Diego said something funny, and fresh tuna sprayed everywhere including over a disgusted and decidedly green-looking Diego himself.

I digress. I shan't ever again eat anything fishy from a can when I have no fine motor coordination and where jokes are being cracked in the immediate area. I found the half-eaten tin of tuna on top of the fridge this morning. Giulia's going to kill me. She has this thing about botulism.

GIULIA: 'Peas. There. Is. A. Half-empty. Can. Of. Tuna. Sitting. On. The. Butter.'

PEAS: 'It's cool; it's still fresh. You want some?'

GIULIA: 'Good Lord, no. I can smell the E. coli from here. Remove it. Now.'

ARE WE, AREN'T WE?

Something's happened. Just like that. I'm not certain what kick-started it, but things have suddenly taken a horrible left turn with Randy. I'm completely anxiety-ridden. And terrified that this may be it.

Last night I had Randy round for my supreme Norwegian salmon and sautéed courgettes on a bed of garlic mash potato – the one dish that gets me excited about poring over a hot stove. Then we started talking. About stuff that's possibly made him run straight out of my life and head for the hills. What have I done?

It all started fairly innocuously. You see, Giulia has this thing about certain words. She winces when people say 'panties', 'moist' and 'making love'. Perhaps it's her tough, no-nonsense Italian heritage, but Chinese torture for Giulia would be to say one or all of those words over and over again within her immediate proximity. So, as Randy, Giulia and I were chilling on the couch, I jokingly said something like, 'Let's go make love, Randy.' Mainly to get a reaction from Giulia. She squirmed, but so did Randy.

RANDY: 'Yuck. Making *lurve*. It's so *The Bold & The Beautiful*. "Oh

Ridge," says Brooke, "let's make lalalalallove!"'
PEAS: 'No, it's not.'
GIULIA: 'Eew, I think I just threw up a little in my mouth.'
PEAS: 'You guys are pathetic. Two people show each other how much they mean to each other by "making love" instead of just bonking.'
GIULIA: 'Stop! I can't take it anymore!'
RANDY: 'Well, I never make love.'
PEAS: 'I know. Because you don't love me.'

Dinner ended on a sour note. He got up to go, kissed me frostily and left. I'm not sure what happens now. However, I will not cry. I will hold it together. Because if this is the end, it's not because he doesn't love me anymore. You can't lose something you never had, right?

The age-old adage of Randy McIntyre and Peas on Toast: he just can't fall in love with me. And this seems to be the common denominator in all of our fights. I've had enough, I am starting to feel lonelier than a single person. He just doesn't understand why I feel so bleak that we just seem to trundle on, and I don't get how he just manages to carry on without any change. Bottom line: I love him, but he hasn't fallen for me. Your classic, if not clichéd, love tragedy. Like the book says, 'he's just not that into me'. It's devastating, but even more devastating is why I haven't just walked away. I'm too terrified to be without him, even if it's only a piece of him.

I wonder if he'll ever phone me again? Or if this is The End. Perhaps it's better not to know, and to just guess if after three days I still haven't heard from him. Why am I such a needy bitch?

IT JUST DOESN'T GET BETTER THAN THIS
On top of my crappy night with Randy and the fact that I might have failed at two relationships in one year, my week got even better. Why?

Car service. I drive a new Beetle. He's my number-one boy. (And may be my only boy after last night's episode.) He's a strong, Germanically made precision vehicle in a cute body. Hence his name, Ludwig. He also costs a flaming fortune to maintain, or so I've learnt today.

Car service grand total: R8 964

You've got to be kidding me. I feel nauseous. Excuse me while I reach for the cigarettes I no longer smoke. I simply can't afford that. Even if I sold my body on Oxford Road for five solid weeks. And I wouldn't come cheap.

I get paid in thirteen days. Let's hope the brakes don't fail before then.

To make matters worse, it's been two days and still no word from Randy.

Chapter Seven

TEARS IN THE TRAFFIC

'Fifty per cent of me wants to stay with you; the other fifty per cent thinks it's better if we end it now.'

Randy broke up with me. And these were the words he used to do it.

I am absolutely devastated.

Giulia: 'I just don't get it. I'll skip my meeting and be home in the next hour.'

Lizzy: 'I am so sorry, Poen. Don't worry, I'm not going to dish out any lectures. What alcohol can I bring you? But I must say I never thought you'd last so long.'

Bennet: 'The Cortina has broken down again. Can you pick me up? Help me to help you to help me.'

Connor: 'I don't believe it. You sure? You sure he's actually said, "We are over?" That's so ... final.'

Diego: 'Do you want me to come over? I'm in the neighbourhood. Do you have snacks?'

Mum (sobbing): 'Peas ... I'm so ... sorry. Why are you so unlucky in love? Why are you attracting this towards you?'

SORRY WHAT?

Sorry WHAT? What just happened? A day ago Randy broke up with me. This can't possibly be happening. Being mowed down by a bus couldn't feel any worse. I am completely broken, I can't even see straight. My entire existence has come crumbling down in a mighty avalanche – I don't see myself surviving past the next second. The Worst Day of My Life I was talking about a few months ago? I think this is it. I've failed at my second relationship. The grief. I feel as though my heart has been chipped out of my chest with a pick axe.

Yet, I forced myself to go to work to perform the menial task of writing an inane article about original recipe monkey gland sauce. A futile attempt to pretend that the world still turns. Somehow this crushing blow seems worse than anything I've experienced before. Worse than with Anthony. Perhaps it was because I was the one who ended that relationship. Randy – the man I have fallen head over heels for, someone I could see myself happily being with next year, next century – has dumped me. I have never been dumped before. Mere words cannot express how badly this hurts.

'Aah. This must be what they mean when they talk about the double break up,' said Giulia. 'You don't really have enough time to mourn the first one, so the second one feels so much worse – you're reliving them both at the same time.'

Thanks for the intellectual insight, Aristotle, but it doesn't really make me feel any better.

I'm a statistic. A stereotype. The girl who ran into the arms of another to try and replicate what she had before. I am furious with myself for falling for Randy so hard while he has just callously fobbed me off. In the aftermath of Five-Years Anthony and Randy, the funniest guy in the world, I really believe this is going to be the end of me.

I must have cried the entire day. I didn't even stop crying at the mechanic while they installed my new brake pads. Upon arriving home, I immediately called Anthony and told him what happened in between wailing. Thankfully, he was very sympathetic and whisked me off for lunch. Once there, he ordered me a succession of double G & Ts and listened attentively while I sobbed and tried to make sense of the sorry demise of my relationship. He didn't try to take advantage of my super-vulnerable situation even after pronouncing himself single. He simply empathised and consoled me. Is he made of steel? I, meanwhile, got absolutely inebriated.

Once home, I asked my friends to come and partake in my self-medication. Giulia made pasta, which I picked at, Connor and Bennet tried to tell me funny jokes. Lizzy, like a true mate, drank with me. I was eventually carried to my bed, whimpering, by Connor.

The hardest thing for me to understand right now is why. *Why?* He told me, just before parting, standing at my door for the last time, that ours was the most intense relationship that he has ever had and insisted that he likes me 'more than enough'. I can understand that. We laugh at the same things. We enjoy doing the same things. He even mentioned how he loves it that I sing karaoke when I'm drunk. He just *gets* me.

Yet, it's not enough. He never thought about us in the future, except once he asked if I'd ever want to live with him in Russia. *Russia?* He always wanted to go and work there for some reason.

My admission of being in love with him made him run. We just weren't on the same page. I wanted so much more. It really, really hurts. And I miss him terribly already. His humour, his face. He has the tiniest little freckles on his nose and those cute froggy hands ... (He has no hair on his hands. I always found this a little strange, but now I miss his fucking hands. Go figure.) I miss the incredible blue intensity of his eyes. It seems like we hooked up just yesterday but it was actually only six months ago while I was still crying about Anthony. It's over. It's all really over. I'm reeling.

Does he even think of me? Or is he relieved? The worst would be if he feels pity or guilt ... I would rather he felt nothing than that.

I AM: not coping.

I WANT: him to run back to me and admit he's made the biggest mistake of his life.

I WISH: I'd never told him how I feel.

I HATE: myself right now and him to a lesser degree.

I FEEL: overwhelmingly depressed.

I MISS: his jokes and him calling me Popsicle.

I FEAR: I will feel sad forever.

I HEAR: my colleague coughing her lungs out and my boss murmuring to himself.

I WONDER: whether he thinks of me.

I REGRET: ever meeting him.

I AM NOT: the best company currently.

I DANCE: on bar counters or at karaoke bars.

I CRY: all the fucking time lately.

I WRITE: about heartache and pain.

I NEED: a double gin and tonic.

I SHOULD: just get over myself.

SOCIAL REINTEGRATION

What's up with friends throwing parties right after I go through a break up? Last time it was Helen's and tonight was Lizzy's. But I suppose they can't put their lives on hold just because of my dramas. And they're my best friends, so I have to make an effort. I haven't brushed my hair in three days, and haven't caught a glimpse of natural sunlight for as long either.

Every time I try to smile or someone asks me how I am, tears well up in my eyes, and I just crumble. I'm so emotionally fragile right now, that if somebody poked me in the ribs, I'd in all likelihood collapse. I sadistically hope that someone may do this; I'd hopefully fall into a coma and wake up a very different person. A person without all this terribly heavy baggage.

So I dragged myself to Lizzy's birthday do. The worst part of the evening was bumping into all of Randy's mates. Thank God he wasn't there. I couldn't bear seeing him right now; I just wouldn't be able to face it. Good of him not to come – even he couldn't be so insensitive. Yet, I walked straight into a snake pit filled with pitying faces not forty-eight hours after the break up.

The only thing I could do to blot out the aching in my gut was to get absolutely wasted. This only made me a worse person to be around, if that is at all possible. At one point in the evening, I blurted out a barrage of loud, expletives when a (stupid) man groped my bottom. Bennet's sordid advice also irritated me no end. 'Just flirt with someone new, Peas. You can't get over one before you get under another.' I would've rather sucked toxic waste through a straw. I told Bennet he was a 'barshtard', before he and Connor dragged me out of the party and forced me into Moloko, a swish club in Rosebank, decorated, in Hansel's words, 'Jewish baroque' – heavy velour and gold gilt interiors. Connor promptly footed my tequila bill, and I happily numbed myself, only hesitating when I tried to snort a shot in the middle of the dance floor.

Dignity is the price I'm paying for being dumped. I'm humiliated, stupid, worthless and pathetic. Lizzy pointed out that I at least held it together enough not to cry in front of Randy's mates. But honestly, I'm a complete mess. The pain is so extreme it feels as though there's a chunk of lead sitting in my belly. I can't remember it ever being this bad before. It hurts when I breathe. On top of it, all the hurt from my Anthony break up has come back to haunt me. Even Giulia's pep talk couldn't relieve me of any suffering.

'What do you plan to do?'

'Um, cry? Forever?'

'Yes, there'll be lots of this. But I mean, have you made any resolutions as to what you're going to do with regards to not letting this happen again?'

'Well I'm never dating again, if that's what you're talking about.'

'It' alright to be extreme right now, but it's not exactly realistic, is it?'

'Fuck it. No one understands.'

The pain only seems to ease when I'm around other people or drunk out of my mind. As long as my mates are being patient with me, it's somewhat uplifting. It's a strong exercise in self-discipline, to be normal around people. I'm trying to fall apart only when I am alone in the safety of my hit-by-a-bomb flat. How Giulia is putting up with me at the moment makes her nothing short of saintly.

Connor, on the other hand, seemed more upbeat about my being dumped:

CONNOR: 'I'm very sad he broke your heart, Peas, but if I'm going to be honest ... he was a strange little man.'

PEAS: 'Why is that? Are you saying you thought he was strange and you never told me? Why did you think he was strange? God, you thought he was strange!'

CONNOR: 'I don't know, maybe I did. But you loved him, Peas, so when I say strange, I don't mean *strange,* weird strange, just strange. Can we change the subject now please?'

PEAS: 'This blows. This whole ordeal blows.'

On the weekend, I did a Monica from *Friends* and scrubbed my flat from top to bottom and washed all my clothes. At least Randy's smell has been removed. Despite the sporadic crying breaks, my apartment is spanking clean.

UP IN SMOKE

I've rediscovered another support system. I'm almost sheepish to admit it but today I smoked an entire box of cigarettes. After managing not to smoke for almost three months, I'm back in the game. (That'll show Randy,' said Lizzy. 'You show him, Peas.') I walked over to the corner café, eyes swollen from crying, and promptly told Joao, the owner, what I'd come for. He refused to sell me cigarettes! Of all the nerve.

My relationship with the café owner across from my apartment is interesting. It's strictly superficial, yet strangely familiar. He's Portuguese and when I breeze in, he regales me with stories about land reform in his home town of Beira, his boat stationed in Lisbon and his frenetic children. Not to mention telling me all about the messy divorce from his wife, with whom he proudly acknowledges having had an open relationship. From what I can gather, the open-door policy was one sided until the day she decided to partake in a bout of casual shagging *sans* husband.

Our conversations haven't changed in three years. Am I the only one to bear the brunt of his candid tales of sexual exploits and anchor-moorings on the Algarve? The biased preference for talking to and serving only me is so blatant – he actually shoos other customers away when we're in conversation, I always turn around, and mouth 'sorry', face etched with guilt, to the waiting queue. I know that once he starts, I'll most likely miss the first twenty minutes of *Home and Away*, which starts at 7:00 p.m. sharp.

If you're in a hurry, don't go in there. Unless, of course, you're bored or lonely. Because Joao always asks the same questions, usually: Do I have a boyfriend? If the answer is no, why not? Depending on my answer, ranging over the years from 'All men are cunts' to 'I don't have the time for a man', he'll go, 'Don't you miss the sex?' all while customers look on, tapping their feet impatiently to pay for his (questionably hygienic) house brisket. Then he asks, if I perhaps want to have sex with him.

If I do have a boyfriend, he steers the conversation towards work. 'You. You're going to be famous. I can see it.' The fact that Joao the horny corner café owner can see it and Hollywood can't isn't tremendously uplifting.

Occasionally, no I lie, frequently, especially after hours, when booze has overcome me, I stumble in there giggling with Lizzy, Giulia or Diego. We'll buy the *Farmer's Weekly* or *Combine Harvester's Tatler* because we think it's kind of funny.

Why do I continue to go there despite his inappropriate ramblings? Well, Joao is never put off by the fact I often come in without my face on, in my red *101 Dalmatians* pyjamas or, often, in the clothes I was wearing, dancing and schvitzing in the night before. Bless his little heart.

If I walk in crying, he's always very sympathetic, but then I suppose he has his own agenda. He also knows I gave up smoking three months ago.

PEAS: 'Marlboro Lights, please.'

JOAO: 'No. I no sell you cigarettes.'

PEAS: 'And why not?'

JOAO: 'No.'

PEAS: 'Fuck that.'

JOAO: 'You no tell me to fuck.'

So the bastard refused to sell me a box. In between gulps of crying, I threatened to go to the petrol station down the road instead. He patted my shoulder, gave me a free chocolate and told me to dry my eyes.

I'm a train wreck; my life is train wreck. But the man at the corner café cares.

ON ANGER

Last night I managed to laugh for a whole two minutes. This was thanks to Lizzy regaling me with memories of her first sexual experience. ('At least Randy never introduced you to German *scheise* movies.') I'm starting to feel a little better and that means I'm getting angry. This is Stage Two, according to a psychological Internet forum. So the fun begins. Because anger is way more liberating than crying in a foetal position on an unmade bed, for instance.

The anger sits coiled inside me like a venomous cobra. Anger at being dumped, for being so stupid, for being too weak to walk away before this happened. As rage and hurt stir within – hell hath no fury like a Peas scorned – I need to remind myself not to lash out. But, the whole *modus operandi* of the grieving process – sadness, anger, denial, acceptance – is an outright lie. I feel all of those stages at once.

And I think I deserve a little rage at present. Why? I loved him. He did not love me. He dumped me. I did not dump him. This is why I am so pissed off.

Randy was never nasty. He didn't cheat on me – he just axed me. In fact, I almost respect him for his cutting-edge honesty. It's not his fault he didn't love me. Hell, I don't love me, so why the fuck would he?

Reliving The End is exhausting:

RANDY: 'I just can't do this. Have you love me and me not reciprocate.'

PEAS: 'And why not? What's the big deal?' (I wish I hadn't said that.)

RANDY: 'Well, it's a big elephant sitting in the room with us. I can never give you what you want. And rather than draw this out for months to come, I think it's best we break up now.'

PEAS: 'Am I not special to you? Am I just another random girlfriend?'

RANDY: 'You are special, Peas, and I love being with you. But I'm not in love with you.'

It crushed me to hear that, my biggest fear made real. But, he's right, going on the way we were would only have made it worse. I wasn't going to hold onto his ankles as he ducked out of the door screaming, 'Why, why, you bastard, *why?*'

I can't think about it anymore, I've replayed the break up over in my head over a thousand times at least and each time it's torture. I've completely regressed – it's like two cold helpings of nightmare tartare. I am back to square one. Giulia says it's a chance to start over with a clean slate, man free. Clean slate, sure – but what about all the bulging suitcases trailing behind me?

Lizzy suggested I warm my chilly winter bed with compulsive masturbation, but really, that would only remind me of how alone I really am.

I'm starting to believe the grieving process is such: sadness, alcoholism, anger, alcoholism, denial, alcoholism. And the pattern continues ad infinitum (unless you fall over in a booze-induced stupor and get run over, which I still fantasise about in my darkest hours). Randy left my life exactly a week ago. It's like he just disappeared – poof, into thin air. For all I know, he could be on the next boat to Russia. I hope he is.

We went to the Jolly Roger last night.

LIZZY: 'I'm just dashing off to the toilet while Helen gets our drinks. Please hold the table.'

PEAS: 'Don't you dare. I can't stand to be on my own for a minute at the moment. Nobody's going anywhere, Giulia, stay right here, or I will burst into tears very loudly and cause a scene.'

HELEN: 'Well, good thing we're friends now, right? I can at least help too.'

GIULIA: 'I once knew how you feel ... the crushing loneliness of suddenly being dumped ...'

PEAS: 'Yeah, let's just rub it in.'

LIZZY: 'Well, look on the bright side. You won't have a guy around who grabs your poen and yells "Cookie!" the whole time.'

HELEN: 'Thank goodness for that.'

PEAS: 'I know you guys thought it was weird, but I loved it.'
This is going to be the coldest, loneliest winter I've ever had to face.
I need a drink. Fast.

Would it be better to pay therapy bills to an expensive shrink or
would it be best, and less traumatic on the bank balance, to take
out these emotions on The Sub? I choose the latter. Although, on
slinking into work today The Sub says: 'I heard you got dumped ...
again.' It took all my resolve to say as calmly as possible, '*No* ... I got
dumped for the *first* time. So now I know what you must feel like,
since you're so much older than me, and would have to know what
it's all about, wouldn't you?'

POPS DOES OUT OF AFRICA

My father has done it again: the predictability of his unpredictabil-
ity has left me floored.

I phoned him to wail and attempt to extract a little fatherly sympathy (knowing full well that he's not capable of this) but I almost
regretted making the call.

While trying to explain to him why he'll never be a grandfather,
he was flying – illegally, mind you – over Lesotho. The country's
government doesn't allow for non-commercial air transport over
Lesotho without prior permission because of the naval base. Dad
didn't want to deal with the bureaucratic red tape. ('It'll take at least
a week to get official word; bugger it, I'm just going to fly.') So here
he was, flying over illegal territory.

PEAS: 'Dad! Bloody hell, you'll get shot down!'

DAD: 'No, I won't. I'll fly low and fast. Low and fast is the answer,
Peas. I need to be in Kokstad by noon.'

PEAS: 'Are you flying over it *right now*?'

Lots of static, sound of wind rushing past, an engine.

DAD: 'Yes. Now this Randall character ... Don't worry, Peas, just find another one.'

PEAS: 'Right. Dad, I'm going to hang up now, I needn't explain why. And that is the worst advice you could give me. You can't just replace someone! That's why I'm in this fix to start with!'

DAD: 'Wow, Lesotho is beautiful.'

PEAS: 'Dad does the air traffic controller know you're using a cell phone at the minute?'

DAD: 'No.'

PEAS: 'Dad have you ever been dumped?'

DAD: 'Clear skies ... Yes; once. By my girlfriend of three years. It was hell.'

PEAS: 'Did you have a rebound relationship?'

DAD: 'Plenty. It's the only way you learn that it's easier to be alone.'

PEAS: 'I don't want to be alone; it's too awful for words!'

DAD: 'Why do you think I fly all the time?'

Fair enough. Perhaps I need to find a hobby. That takes over my life. I'll become a fanatic! I feel a glimmer of hope. I wonder if sleeping all day can be classed as a hobby?

Meanwhile Mum is trying to convince me to attend one of her meditation classes. 'Peas, I know you're hurting, but you won't believe the illumination that comes from connecting with the divine self.' Just to ease her mind, I accepted all the pamphlets she gave me on meditation, and promised her I'd look into it. She also gave me garlic to eat to keep my 'immunity up'. So now I'm depressed *and* I stink.

My bed has become my break up buddy. I can pull the duvet right over my face and cry without Giulia hearing me. I feel safe and warm. Breaking up with someone in winter is worse than summer; I should've avoided this at all costs and dumped him in March. But alas, it's May, and I know Highveld winters are cold, but this year it's particularly ferocious. Granted, I don't sleep on his side of the bed, but I can lie here and let tears smudge mascara onto his pillow.

I AM FABULOUS ... AREN'T I?

Last night after two weeks of overwhelming self-pity I came up with a new idea to tackle the grieving process. Previously, I only arrived at frivolous conclusions like building a bar in my bedroom so I never have to leave the house again. I've decided to pretend to pull myself together. In my bed, I will cry. In the outer world, I will be ... awesome.

I need to rebuild my shattered self-esteem somehow, so let this be my first project. 'Fake it 'til you make it' is my new mantra. Pretending I have some self-esteem might actually fool me into believing that I actually have some. Yay! I have turned a little corner. I hate myself for being dumped, but the best thing I can do for my pride is to force myself to think that life is just wonderful. A healthy solution, I reckon.

Lizzy came round for a comforting glass of red and I shared my new revelation.

'If Randy doesn't think I'm fabulous then there has got to be something wrong with him because I am fabulous. Right? I will not shed one more tear over that little shit. Why? Someone else out there will think I'm amazing. I'm backing myself one hundred per cent. I have no time for men who wouldn't recognise a good thing if it slapped them.'

'I'm so proud of you. You've brainwashed yourself into thinking you deserve more. This is a positive step.'

'Are you suggesting I don't really believe myself? Or that you don't believe it?'

'Um ... as long as it gets you through and stops the crying, whatever it is, I'm happy.'

Am I just deluding myself? Probably. Yet, I'm certainly going to try it.

Tonight I will go clubbing so I don't fall off the radar and I can self-medicate at the same time. But first, I have to eat dinner at a restaurant with a posse of boring people that I hardly know. I don't want to leave my house, but in order not to be alone tonight, I simply have to attend. This is what I've planned to reply if people catch wind that I'm suddenly single:

'If he's doing half as well as I am that's great ... I'm amazing.'

'I wonder how Randy is? He must be heartbroken to have left a good-looking lush such as myself.'

'Aren't I just ... incredible?'

On the other hand, any of these other scenarios may occur:
1) I will bump into Randy or his friends, immediately freak out and evacuate.
2) I will bump into Randy and his friends and immediately get pissed.
3) On getting pissed, following on from the scenario above, I will back myself one hundred per cent and they will be astounded in the face of my unshakeable self-esteem and likeable arrogance.
4) I will knock a prawn cocktail into someone's lap.
5) I will look beautiful. So beautiful that everyone will immediately faint upon resting their eyes on my lovely face.
6) I will set the establishment alight with a stray match.
7) I will receive a mysterious call from my childhood sweetheart, who happens to know my number, who happens to know where I live, and who happens to want to shag me up against a wall.
8) I'll delight everyone with my endless wit and charm; perhaps buy the whole table shooters, then leave and go find some ass.

Lizzy thinks I've gone completely crackers: 'I think you should spend a night or two at home watching the E! channel.'

'I think I should see how many benders I can have in a row.'

From: peasontoast@gmail.com
To: connor@irishcarbomb.com
Subject: Guess what?

... I am fabulous. I have decided that I'm actually a little fox.
Both inside and outside of the bedroom. I am amazing, Connor.
This may sound conceited, or perhaps downright obnoxious,
but you know, conceitedness is a by-product of fabulousness.
Besides, Paris Hilton seems to get away with it and I'm even
more fabulous than her. Not that I need to tell you this, you
already know ...

From: connor@irishcarbomb.com
To: peasontoast@gmail.com
Re: Guess what?

You been smoking your socks? I see you're not holding up as
well as I thought. Can I bring you anything after work?

From: giulliabriattore@itye.com
To: peasontoast@gmail.com
Subject: Where's my flatmate?

I'm officially worried. I never see you and I live with you. If
you're not out drowning your sorrows in some manky pub,
you're crying in your room. And I can hear you so don't deny it.
Please come back; I miss you, my flatmate! It's fine if you carry
on about me having mini Amor Vittones with Hendrik one day.
In fact, you're allowed to talk about it all the time, if it means
you'll show some (sober) face around our dwelling.

From: peasontoast@gmail.com
To: giuliabriattore@itye.com
Re: Where's my flatmate?

It's all right if you have Amor Vittone clones as your spawn.
I'll be the best godmother ever, because I don't see myself ever
having babies. Oh, my shattered fat fuck. Rugga buggers aren't
de rigueur.
I have to go to a really hectic dinner tonight. But don't worry, I
am so absolutely amazing that I will handle it perfectly.
xxxx

THE DINNER

Now that I'm deeply into pretending that Randy's departure hasn't
affected me one little iota, I left the office early, in a manically
good mood. Yes, I know I'm self-deluded at the moment, but feeling
outrageously positive about my single future sure beats feeling sad.
Even The Sub left me alone today – perhaps the mad grimace I have
plastered on my face scared her away.

Connor popped in after work to bring me some nougat. I'd much
rather have stayed on the couch with him watching The History
Channel, but I had to prove to myself I could go out in public and
behave. The grandiose feeling was short lived. I started feeling less
fabulous about myself during the dinner but tried really hard not
to show it and was successful. The high point of the evening was
when the girl sitting to my left asked if *I'd* broken up with my ex-
boyfriend considering how unfazed and happy I seemed.

Beaming, I replied, 'He dumped me, but I'm great! Wonderful!
God it feels good to be so incredible.'

She shot me a puzzled glance and then turned her attention back
to her *pain au tapenade.*

Besides that interaction, the dinner was predictably anxiety-filled as some of Randy's friends were there all oohing and aahing over the 'amazing sushi'. Quite frankly, I've had better sushi in Sasolburg.

The blatant obnoxiousness I exuded peaked quickly and then plummeted into the bottom of the multiple Jaegerbombs that I oh so blithely chugged down like a machine afterwards at The Manhattan Club, aka The Meat Market. Anthony was there, buying Lizzy and I drink after drink. I think I might've even flirted with Anthony a teensy weensy bit, but hopefully nothing overbearing. I don't want to seem desperate.

Then, oh sweet Jesus, I kissed a guy who I sort of know, but who, sober, is about as attractive to me as a vat of tile grouting (although not completely hideous looking, beer goggles aside). Anthony had his tongue too far down another girl's throat to notice.

Completely freaked out at the concept of sharing saliva with another male, I left the guy mid-snog and ran out of the club so fast that I almost left my face behind, along with the last remaining threads of my dignity. It feels way too foreign to be even talking to other men right now.

Admittedly, snogging a faceless man might not have been the most sensible thing to do at this point in time, but it's not like I had a choice: this is what young, single people do. I'm only trying to fit in.

At 4:00 a.m., I woke up and thought I was dying. When last was I this hung-over? Matric holiday?

Despite that minor paranoid setback, I'm not about to stop now. I'm just getting into the swing of things, proving to the world and myself that I couldn't care less about what's happened. So, I hauled myself off to a quaint curry hovel in Melville with Bennet, Connor and Gwendolyn. She wasn't her usual sarky self so maybe she feels a tad bit of compassion towards me, which irks me no end. She did say she was sorry to hear about me and Randy to which I replied, 'Who the dickens is Randy? Oh ... *that* guy.'

Connor took me aside and demanded I smell his feet, which, to his credit, smelt like Tuscany in springtime, and then asked concernedly how I was doing. He knows me so well I didn't even have to answer. Gwendolyn ended up getting upset about moles. Not the epidermal mole – the furry rodent that digs holes in people's lawns. Bennet mentioned that he had to clear up the divots in his garden because of the moles, and Gwendolyn threw down her fork and asked him why he had to bring up the 'M' word.

For the love of.

Luckily Connor got a piece of popadum stuck in his throat, a fortunate distraction from the 'M' word. The Indian restaurateur had to administer a strong Heimlich manoeuvre on him while Gwen continued to admonish Bennet.

Perhaps it's all part of pretending, but I've mentally prepared myself to hit more nightclubs with reckless abandon. This is what footloose and fancy-free people do when they're single, right? They *party*. They do what they want to do! I also went shopping with Giulia yesterday and returned with a new jacket so smoking it makes me want to have sex with myself. Speaking of which, I've dusted the cobwebs off my Bushwhacker 3 000. Nightclubs and masturbation, thank heavens for them.

THINKING BEFORE ONE SPEAKS

I have to be careful what I say and do in my office during my post-break up delirium out of innate fear of Madame La Sub as she'll most certainly relay it back to my boss. So I've played down my break up significantly. Apparently, she broke it off with her fiancé last year and since then has been revelling in the single life. 'I'm channelling my grief by absorbing myself in my work,' she overheard me telling Deidra, which irritated her, because she can find no fault with this statement. However, for the most part, I just keep quiet about it.

Bennet's pretty compassionate about my work-related issues

because his corporate environment is very competitive which sometimes stresses him out.

'Your sub-editor may be a biyatch, but try working in a male-dominated insurance company for two and a half seconds, Peas.'

'I'd welcome it.'

'My beautiful open-plan office has fluorescent lighting, a dead plant and a coffee machine that doesn't work properly, especially in winter.'

'Yeah, that's a bummer. Coffee or bust. I miss Randy.'

'Shut up, and concentrate. Let me paint the picture. All the employees are men, except for one: a painfully quiet Indian lass, who ninety per cent of the day, tinkers away at her keyboard, which only piques the interest of the testosterone-fuelled environment.'

'Has she ever had her heart broken?'

'Dunno, who cares? But, I seem to put my foot in it all the time. I strolled into the office and exclaimed loudly into the silence, "What's that smell?" For indeed, I smelt something strong and potent. To which this young little lass, who should've known better, sat up, peered over her cubicle-divider and said, "Oh I'm sorry, it's my guava."'

'Oh my word. She really said that?'

'She then bit into her guava, still completely unawares as to the sexual reference and why her male audience found it all so hilarious.'

'Thanks dude. You really did make me forget Randy for almost ten seconds.'

HEADS UP

Lizzy phoned me irate today. She was crying, so I went over to her house. It turns out that she's been hiding a real flesh-and-bone living boyfriend from me. And he has just broken up with her.

What?

'You had a boyfriend? A guy you called a "boyfriend" and you haven't told me? How long has this been going on for?'

Lizzy whispered through tears, 'Two months.'

Oh Christ. How could she hide something like this from me for so long? Everyone knew about me and Randy from the get-go.

'Lizzy, frankly I'm devastated. How could you not tell me?'

'Peas, I didn't want to dedicate my life so soon to a man like you did and be the mess you are now. I didn't want to integrate him completely which includes meeting all my friends only to have a break up and end up a mess like you.'

'But, you could have told me about him at least.'

'Peas! You have so much going on in your life, your issues, your dramas, I can't squeeze in a word, never mind a break up! Why does it always have to be about you?'

I felt my stomach turn as she sat crying on the edge of the bath tub, clearly grief stricken. I'm a terrible friend. Welling up, I fled.

I'm heartbroken. I suppose being so wrapped up in my own emotional whirlpool, I hadn't noticed the signs of her suffering. Clearly being an only child has left more scars then I previously thought. Damn and blast those parents of mine. It's left me revoltingly self-absorbed and selfish, an absolute brat. I must be exhausting as a friend. Oh God, I'm no use to anybody! This is too much to bear! I just want to die, frankly.

After crying into my pillow wondering whether my upstairs neighbour hates me, I started to pull myself together. Maybe I am hopelessly selfish, but I have many good qualities too: passion, flair, an outgoing nature ... So I'll better myself now that I've been made painfully aware of my flaws. Everybody has their issues and I know I can be half normal if I really put my mind to it.

I know I need to call Lizzy and apologise, but she's hurt me too. I've decided to avoid her for now. Besides, she obviously thinks I'm horrible so I'll stay away for a while.

Feeling nostalgic and sad yesterday, I looked through some of my old diaries to remind myself that I actually had a fairly okay life before all of this drama.

I've written in a diary since I was six years old. My mum painstakingly kept every one of these journals in a box together with my old Barbie dolls, school blazer, letters and birthday cards. Writing by hand became somewhat of a bother after a while so eventually I just started saving my daily thoughts on my PC.

Every now and then, I haul out the box, or flitter through the thousands of Word documents. Categorically, I have a record of my entire life so far. If, by some miracle of God, I become famous for my literary prowess, I won't need to write an autobiography. Some poor sod can tack it together using the reams of illegible documents stored on my computer and in boxes in the closet.

But this isn't about me being famous at the minute, tempting as it is to dream about the paparazzi catching me mid hair-curler in a skimpy negligee, nipping out in the dead of night to buy a latte. This is a rough timeline of snatches of diarised content. Although juvenile and deconstructed, it forecasts my entire life from the age of six and reading through it all now, I really wonder whether I'm crazy.

1987, 15 March: Humphrey my hamster died. My friend squeezed it and throwed it on the floor.

1989, 18 January: Shane showed me his tree house. I showed him my cookie. He says he's never seen one before.

1992, 6 June: I'm in Amsterdam. Dad put his hand over my eyes when we were walking down the street. But I already saw the naked lady in the window. It smells funny here.

1993, 18 May: We're on our St Lucia school trip. I got my period for the first time last night. How do I tell Mr Andrews why I can't snorkel tomorrow? This is so embarrassing I might as well just die this second.

1994, 24 January: I'm finally at boarding school. The other girls seem nice and I have unpacked my trunk. Met a nice girl called Lizzy. But I'm missing home like mad. Had to polish the Head Girl's shoes and I asked her what a 'blow job' means. She said I'd find out in good time. Whatever.

1994, 28 August: I grabbed someone! I'm not green anymore! Luckily he had braces too, so it wasn't too blind. I wore my Doc Martens and a body suit. He phoned last night, but I was too scared to talk to him, so I asked a prefect to take a message.

1995, New Year's Day: Huge party last night with my parents and their crazy friends. We stole Hunter's Gold. I think I got drunk 'cos Mum said I was showing off and being impossible.

1996, 6 July: I fucking hate everybody. My parents are giving me hell, I hate school and I just want to run away from here. I can't even listen to my music loud. They are being completely unreasonable.

1997, 14 November: Oh shit. Lizzy and I are getting suspended because we bunked school. The folks are seriously fucked off. I've been grounded. This is *so* not fair. Can't they see I just want to be free? I'm a sensible person. I can handle nightclubs! Now I can't even see my boyfriend. They always have to ruin my fun. My boyfriend phoned the house, and I had to hang up on him. Dad always listens, and it's downright embarrassing.

1998, 2 November: Biology final tomorrow. Sometimes I wonder how learning the geometrics of the ear is going to somehow shape my life. I have to sit and learn the mechanics of the cochlear off by heart. Somebody help me. Oh, and did I mention my folks are getting divorced tomorrow? Yes, significant that. They've chosen a simply brilliant time – particularly with me being in the middle of my Matric final exams.

1999, 7 January: I am coping with life in France. Just barely, save the date I went on with some Jean-Michel where I had to eat glazed frogs legs in a pre-Revolution gothic crypt. Then he tried to get in my pants. I'm over it. I was over it before it even began.

2000, 12 February: It's orientation week at varsity. Last night, after Lizzy and I drank papsak in someone's digs, we couldn't remember where our res was, or even that I'm in Cape Town, never mind the whereabouts of my actual room. I think I snogged Warren. This is not good.

2000, 13 February: Great. Now Warren's stalking me. I'm hiding out in my room for the whole day – he's sitting outside waiting for me to come out.

2000, 17 March: A guy called Anthony made me write my number on his shirt last night. He was so gorgeous, I nearly died. Today he hung a giant poster in his window advertising his intention to phone me. Is twenty-four hours too short to know whether you've found the love of your life?

2001, 23 July: Priscilla hasn't done the fucking dishes again. But I can't say anything in case she yells at me. She's completely hormonal, like, all 365 days of the year. This is a digs, for crying out loud.

2002, 14 January: Anthony and I have been in Colorado for a month. There's fresh powder this morning, so I took a skiing break without clocking out. Getting paid to ski – now that's what I'm talking about. We got stoned in the Happy Hut with a bunch of Kiwis. Not sure how I got out of the fucking conifer plantation alive.

2003, 28 November: Anthony and I are going to Thailand tomorrow. Let it be known I will be having sex every single day and drinking mai tais on the double on Phi Phi Island. Leonardo DiCaprio filmed *The Beach* there. I will sit where he sat.

2004, 7 May: I bought a fuck-off suit yesterday. That'll show The Sub I mean business.
Bitch.

IT'S CALLED A BREAK UP

...'cos it's broken. Finally, after scouring all the Exclusive Books in the area with no luck for *It's Called a Break Up Because It's Broken* (Greg Behrendt and Amiira Ruotola-Behrendt) I found the evasive best-selling book, bought it and promptly read it from cover to cover. I need help. I can't afford a shrink, so a self-help book is going to have to do. Lizzy has thrust me into action, if anything. According to it, the basic points to remember when going through heart-wrenching grief are:

1) Put down the phone. Do not call him. Ever. (Check. Have not even farted in his direction, never mind called, SMSed, e-mailed. I have no urge at all. Even when I'm drunk and emotional.)
2) Don't try to accidentally bump into him. Ever. (Check. Avoiding places we used to hang out together. Have turned down two invitations to the Colony Arms recently because, well, the place is disgusting, and he might be there. Plus, if he is shagging someone new and on the off-chance I see them together, I wouldn't want

to intimidate her with my fabulousness. Or otherwise dissolve in a fit of jealousy and rage.)

3) Don't whine about him all the time to your friends. Get a shrink. (Don't need a shrink. Need vodka and nightclubs.)

4) Don't boil his bunny. Or be any kind of psycho, for that matter. (Check. Haven't burnt any of the belongings he left at my house, haven't called him up and told him I will kill him, or stuck pins in a Voodoo doll.)

5) Look fabulous for someone new, not him. (Check. This is easy. I looked fabulous for the corner café guy the other day, where my averaged-sized noombies looked like they were going to burst out of my new shirt. In a classy way, I swear.)

6) Love yourself before you move on to somebody else. (Um, check! Hello? I wonder when my self-infatuation will end? Is it a phase or am I going nuts?)

7) Avoid self-destructive behaviour during this traumatic time. (Oh come on, everyone needs a vice.)

8) Don't see him ever. Avoid any contact for eighty days.

While I'm reading all this theoretical advice, agreeing with all the above points and believing I'm doing all the right things and feeling ever so proud of myself, an e-mail arrived from Randy. It's the first contact I've had from him since that awful day, a month ago, barring an SMS I received one night at 3:02 a.m., and I'll assume he doesn't remember sending it. ('I don't know what to say but just wanted to make contact.') It was all going so well – me trying to pretend he was dead – when he had to go and contact me, throwing me back into a wanton state of despair.

Seeing the e-mail in my inbox made my heart stop. I reckoned that he wasn't giving me a second thought (as fabulous as I am) and that he had moved on weeks ago.

It asked how I am and what I have been doing lately. 'Hi Peas, how are you doing? I've finally found a job and wanted to know how you're getting on. I hope we can meet soon for coffee or something and touch base? I just want to know we're cool. Randy.'

Sticking strictly to the rules of *It's Called a Break Up*, I replied: 'I'm good, thanks. But please don't contact me again. I'm fine.'

But really I should've written: 'Well, I've been partaking in the odd cigarette when out for a drink or chatting with friends. I am weak and am not coping as well as I profess to be. I am self-medicating with alcohol quite extraordinarily, finding myself time and again amongst the bottom feeders of society at three in the morning. I don't care to wash my make-up off before I go to bed after a big night out at a club. I miss you so much it hurts and I can't stand the thought of you sucking face with other women, and please please come back. WHY DID YOU LEAVE ME?'

But I didn't.

HELP ME TO HELP YOU TO HELP ME

Deciding that I was ready to reconcile, I went over to Lizzy's with a chocolate cake. I don't want her to deal with this break up without me. The least I can do is go over there and show her how I truly regret not being there for her.

'I want to say sorry for dragging you through all my stuff over the past few months. And I want to hear all about your grief with whatever-his-name-is. You're right, I've been selfish. And I need to address why I can be so all-consuming sometimes.'

She pulled me into a bear hug, and said, 'Thanks for being here with me. Sorry if I was harsh, but if you weren't that bad, I wouldn't bother saying it at all.'

'Oh Lizzy! Are you alright? What did this bastard do to you?'

'He got back together with his ex. His name is James. I'm such an idiot.'

'You're not an idiot. Now tell me all about it.' (I tried hard not to say, 'Oh I understand. When I was dumped ...') I wanted to work on listening for a change instead of bombarding her with my stuff.

'Thing is, I don't know if we should even talk about it,' she smiled weakly. 'If I consciously block James out, and pretend he doesn't exist, then he literally doesn't exist.' I'm so glad she said this. So I'm not the only one who sometimes prefers an illusion to the reality.

Nonetheless, I replied, 'You don't think you're avoiding the situation altogether?'

'Maybe, but if he prefers dating a whorette to me, then really, that's his problem, not mine. And besides, there's more important stuff to focus on. Like whether these jeans make me look fat. What a palaver. Let's eat some cake.'

CHAPTER EIGHT

SINGLETONS' WEEKEND

After processing Randy's unexpected e-mail, I made a concerted effort to remind myself why being single isn't so bad. In fact, many women choose to have careers instead of husbands these days, don't they? But I find it terrifying to be alone and would like to be able to embrace it like others seem to. Imagine being able to say, 'Phew. Well thank God that's over. Now I can backpack through Bolivia/ start my own business/focus on myself.' *Focus on myself.* Why would anybody want to do that? For one, you end up having way too much time to think, and therefore over-analyse the sorry state of your existence resulting in horrendous self-absorption.

At least this is what I think. Why do I always need a boyfriend to fill the gaps inside me? Who knows? I was cuddled beneath a fleece blanket on the couch on Saturday morning exploring these possibilities when Giulia flounced in, put on VH1 and forced me do a dance off with her to Phil Collins' Top Ten.

'You would never do this in your most revolting pyjamas with Randy around.'

'True, but you did it and your boyfriend could walk in at any moment.'

'Sure, but sometimes I like to fantasise about being single.'

'Would you want to be single, honestly, if you had the choice?'

'Not for a second. However, you get to do whatever you want and don't have to answer to anybody.'

'What if I like answering to somebody?'

'You can eat *pain au chocolat* and Golden Smackeroos in your bed, wearing a tracksuit, and leave crumbs everywhere if you so wish.'

'Well, I suppose that having no boyfriend also means I can foster stronger bonds with my male friends without anyone getting jealous. That's one good thing. The other day I asked Diego to buy me some tampons. He refused. But despite that he has been an awfully good support of late. It's nice to have made a new friend.'

'When I'm lonely, or when Hendrik's away, Diego always brings me his mother's espetada.'

'Although ... like any boyfriend, he also eats us out of house and home.'

'Friends are usually more reliable than boyfriends, but don't tell Hendrik I said that; he really is the exception.'

'Maybe I'll find someone like Hendrik one day.' (Sigh.)

'He has a couple of really decent Afrikaans friends who are single, you know. There's Frikkie, for example.'

'Save it. I just can't see myself with a Frikkie, sorry.'

'Look on the bright side! You can leave parties whenever you like, you never have to wait for anybody, you don't have to suffer through the "why hasn't he called me?" shit. You're free as a bird!'

'Yeah, I guess ...'

'On another note, I bought you something to cheer you up.'

'Really? For me? Can't I marry *you*?'

'No. But here's a camembert cheese.'

Good old Giulia, she knows me so well and at least all my friendships seem to be back on track.

We then watched a particularly good episode of *Grey's Anatomy*, the one in which Meredith breaks up with Derek because she's scared of commitment – I wanted to throw something at the screen and yell, 'Don't do it, Meredith. You'll regret it!' After retiring to bed, I played with myself – at least we can still sexually satisfy ourselves when alone. I then dreamt that I got eaten alive by a writhing sea monster while Randy just stood on the sidelines and watched impassively.

OUR FAMILY IN SUMMER BAY

After traipsing home and crying into my pillow, I watched with fascination how mascara drips, debris-like when wet. (It's fascinating watching oneself cry in the mirror. You should try it.) I want to feel happy. I really do. So why is it taking so long?

Diego popped in and reminded me that I could very well live vicariously through another person's life by reading a book or planting myself in front on the telly. I suppose another 'fantastic' benefit of being single is that I can watch whatever I like without anyone complaining about my choice in TV. He's absolutely right. I'm addicted to the old Australian soapie *Home and Away*. Go TV started airing *Home and Away* in 2003, and I now watch it at 7:00 p.m. every day, without fail. I even visit the revamped website at work, when The Sub isn't around to see me and tell the big boss during one of their sordid sexual liaisons. It's exactly the kind of mindless entertainment that I enjoy coming home to, armed with a glass of plonk. Randy never really got that.

My fetish did not go unnoticed when Giulia moved in and, at first, she was appalled when she encountered my unnatural possessiveness over the TV remote between 7:00 and 7:30 p.m. When I lived with Anthony, we'd fight over the remote for cricket highlights versus my small-town Ozzie white-trash fix. He soon learnt to obey the matriarch of the household – yours truly – and became intrigued with it himself. And this after endless whining and countless accusations of 'How can you watch this?'

Oh yes.

Diego gave me the same uphill about it – although he doesn't live with us, he practically does.

But, now it's 'Amanda is going to marry Graham for his money, stupid bastard. And did you see what's happened to Kim? Dude, like, have you even been watching?'

'Ah ... yes. In healthy quantities.'

'Shit has hit Summer Bay in huge way, china. It's all action, action, action. Did you check out the website today, Peas?'

And God forbid you talk during the soliloquies. ('Irene is having a moment here guys, talk during the commercials.') He's totally glued.

I'm glad I've been influential in this about turn. Even if it's in the perpetuation of one of the worst shows that television has to offer. I'm also relieved – thank God for soap operas! For half an hour a day, I can discard my crappy life and live through another's! My world doesn't exist for half an hour a day – it's a total escape.

MY NEW BOYFRIEND

Home and Away, my dildo, copious amounts of alcohol and friends. I'm starting to appreciate the small pleasures of being a single however inane they may be. It's not *all bad*. It's these trivial things that keep me going from one week to the next. It could be worse, as I've tried to explain to my mother who is still trying to get me to visit her swami.

'But, Peas, you'll love him. Everything will become so much clearer to you when you attend satsang.'

'Mom, I'm fine, I don't want things to be clearer, I'm quite happy distracting myself from them at the moment. It's not like I've turned to crack to dull the pain or anything.'

(Sigh.)

The truth is that no matter how much I try to escape, I really am starting to realise how unhealthy my relationship with Randy was. And Anthony, for that matter. Why did I settle for it? A confident person wouldn't settle for less; they'd rather be single. Or that's what Dr Eve said on the radio the other day anyway. Happiness with a man is a totally foreign concept to me. So I'd like to introduce my new boyfriend. The Bushwhacker 3 000. He was always around, but on the periphery. Women have the vote, they have careers. And now we can satisfy ourselves sexually without any strings attached. I am embracing my dildo, and thanking the Lord for my clitoris, another one of Dr Eve's dictums.

However, I still dream of Randy, usually nightmares that I don't need a shrink to interpret for me. I swing between feeling terribly sorry for myself and knowing that this is, ironically, the healthiest I've been for years. Still, if Randy came crawling back tomorrow I'd probably accept him with open arms which means I still have a long way to go in my healing. This is dangerously wishful thinking. In the meantime, I'll be satisfied with my inanimate Whacker for comfort. My man of the moment has a three-speed setting and is cleverly embalmed in a comforting jelly exterior. He's also available in various hues, including hot pink. This automatically makes him Dildo Fabulous. (Adult World Melrose North, R299. And they threw in two free tubes of lube.)

Giulia has a vibrator too and we speak freely to each other about our ever-faithful plastic members. It's only right I wax lyrical about loyal Bushie with the utmost love and adoration; after all, he's helping me to sleep at night, isn't he? He's astutely juxtaposed next to the book for fabulous bitches like myself who have recently found themselves microwaving TV meals for one (*It's Called a Break Up Because It's Broken*) on my nightstand.

All the men I have known intimately have been less than enamoured with my dildo. I haven't asked them to be friends as such, but I have made the necessary introductions. It seems that they're usually intimidated by my lowly Whacker. It's not a size issue, it's not a colour issue, and it's not because he has three speed settings.

Men are intimidated because I can pull him out whenever I fancy and he's always in the mood.

It's certainly a useful little gadget for when the lady is hot with desire and the man is not. I have used him in front of two of my lovers (on separate occasions) both of who were, at the time, too tired to get it on.

But, admittedly, as pleasing as it is, it's a man I miss at the moment. He simply cannot be replaced by a jellified penis. But for the moment it'll do.

Connor asked me for the low down on how I'm coping with my sex drought. I reminded him that, luckily for women, we can substitute the man's appendage with an elongated toy. He also, unsurprisingly, turned his nose up at the mention of it. Then I suggested Gwendolyn may possibly have one – most women I know do, after all. He balked and promptly changed the topic to a play he went to at the Market Theatre.

WHY LOVE IS BOLLOCKS

After much thinking, at which I've become so darn good, I've emerged a grumpy old cynic. I'm wondering whether a relationship is feasible for me *ever again*. We've established that I have issues, but now I just feel rage. I don't know how to address it, but for now: Goodbye Naïve Peas, hello Peas With Chip On Her Shoulder. I am now firmly ensconced on the lowest rung of the Happ-Peas-ness ladder. And the new me is nasty.

(Disclaimer: the following is not for light-hearted romantics who think fuzzy, sweet thoughts all day long.)

A purely hypothetical synopsis on why being cynical about love and all of its pathetic idealisms is justifiable:

This Guy and That Girl meet.
Sparks fly.
They get along.
They shag, no wait, they *make love*.
They do stuff together.
They get married.

You. Have. Got. To. Be. Shitting. Me.

Case Study 1: She thinks the chemistry and love is mutual. It's not.
(This is a classic – tragedy, that is.)
This Guy and That Girl meet.
She digs him.
Her flatmate digs him.
Hell, even her friends dig him.
Then he shags someone else.

Case Study 2: 'Love' lasts.
This Guy and That Girl laugh together.
They shag.
They fall in love.
They move in together.
They fall out of love.

This happens time and again when people hook up. This is precisely why I never expect to find that pathetic-sounding 'soul mate' or someone who loves me enough to be with me for the rest of my life. Love is a machine, an establishment. It's a lie. My father can probably tell you the rest. Ha.

I'm choosing to be cynical about love purely because I believe it doesn't exist. This whole 'true love', he was 'the one' deal is just naïve. It never happens. Well done, Hollywood has brainwashed you.

Until a few months ago, I was a hopeless romantic. I wanted all those fairytale things that (silly) little girls dream about. But, it's never going to happen. And I'm dealing with it. It's just part of growing up.

This may seem morbid, bitter even. But it's also sadly true. So here's a little reality check for all of you: the reason you can't find love is because it's not out there. If you're one of the few to have found it, you're exceedingly lucky. I'm only twenty-five, but have fortunately experienced a series of not-so-happily-ever-after situations, which have put me firmly in my place. I should be thankful that they happened so that I could realise the truth.

Not to say that I won't live with some hope of someone saving me from my own cynicism. However, I live in hope, not delusion, so I also know that the chance of this happening is slim.

I can still respect other people thinking that love is amazing. I'm not going to be a constant drag about it. Especially since everyone around me seems to be attached or hooking up. Well, it may last for now, but don't bet your life on it. Because it always falls apart. Eventually.

It takes getting used to, but with enough discipline and a healthy dose of realism, you too can avoid one of the human race's most destructive emotions.

GIRL'S NIGHT

Lizzy called me in tears last night. It would appear her pseudo-boyfriend, Gary ('pseudo', because I believed they were broken up) was seen out and about with another woman:

'Peas, I saw Gary with another woman last night.'

'Okay ... but you've been broken up forever, so why are you crying?'

'I don't know.' (Now howling.)

'Okay. What was he doing and why was it such a surprise?'

'Well,' (gulps for air) 'I think I may still be in love with him. Because he was all over this girl like a bad rash and I had had too much drink and I ... and now I'm embarrassed and then ...' (gulps for air, more tears) '...and then I kissed his best friend right in front of him.'

' That's not good. That's not good at all.'

'*Fuck*.' (Howling.) 'Just tell me what to do, what can I do?'

'I think the best thing to do is this (and this is from me and that book I've been reading): don't contact him or see him for eighty days. It'll clear your head.'

'Shouldn't I apologise or something? I mean, I don't want him to think I'm a total bitch nutcase or something.'

'Yeah. Not a bad idea. SMS him, say you're sorry and then leave him. Poor Liz. I'm sorry!'

'Crap. I thought I always held it together. And here's me, asking *you* for advice.'

'Yeah, who'da thunk it?'

'It gets worse: I went for a run this morning and bumped into him at the shops. I smelt like Wally Hayward's pits after running the Comrades Marathon.'

'That always happens. You see them when you haven't washed your hair for three days. So did you apologise?'

'No. Can we go out tonight please?'

'Need you even ask?'

HOW TO SNOG SOMEONE IN FIVE EASY STEPS

I dragged a depressed Lizzy out to Manhattan last night, even calling Helen to come along too. Lizzy knows Helen way better than I do, but I figured she needed all the back-up she could get. It's odd being the one in control and relatively stable for a change. It felt great to be able to console someone else, to return the favour. The change of dynamics made me believe I was strong enough to manhandle a Mr

Right Now so, I shared a kiss with the second guy since Randy – a complete stranger. He wasn't a bad-looking chap. I even managed to find out what he does (auditing), where he studied (Stellenbosch University), where he lives (Morningside), but don't for the life of me ask me his name. We had skittered off to Manhattan after all, a place where usual pleasantries aren't exchanged, where desperate single-tons cavort with other desperate singletons in the hope of sharing five minutes of saliva with one another.

It's easy to close a deal in this place. I'm already becoming a pro at it. In fact, after all those years of being with Anthony, I never re-ally got to do stuff like this.

How to kiss a guy in five moves:
1) Grope his ass. Seriously.
2) When he turns around, flash him a wicked smile.
3) Dance with him.
4) Kiss him. But don't worry when he lunges first.
5) You can choose to flee after your brief craving for affection has been sated.

Amazingly, I didn't panic this time and sprint from the club, heels a-clattering. Helen dropped Lizzy at home (after I dragged her away – tongue entwined with some boy who couldn't have been over twen-ty years old), tucked her in, and went home with Helen. I felt good being someone that could be counted on. For once.

I'm getting to know Helen better now too. We've bonded over vodka tonics and the dance floor of Manhattan. I was surprised – I actually rather like Helen. After that awful day where Lizzy bought Helen along to my little Randy intervention, and Helen, an almost stranger, started proffering her advice, I never believed we would be friends. But here we are! Two new friends this year – Diego and Helen. That's a real positive, isn't it?

LIZZY: 'How wonderful are we? I think this guy thinks I'm his girlfriend. Tee hee! I'm all better. Thanks, Poen!'

HELEN: 'Vino! Vino! Vino! How doth we love ye!'

PEAS: 'Lizhy I gone hjome with Jelen I amazing.'

LIZZY: 'Wha? Phone me if sdtuck. Ha ha whose that random you snashing in face?'

PEAS: 'We alredy tuckd u in, dude. I safe. U safe. We all okay.'

HELEN: 'Well, I'd liken my current emotional and physical state to a steaming pile of canine shite served on a tea tray. Is this hangover for real?'

TYPES OF NIGHTCLUB PEOPLE

I'm becoming quite accustomed to the various nightclubbing stereotypes.

The Sneaker Outer: This person will evacuate the building alone or with someone else without informing the rest of the group. The group, only realising much later due to crowds and drunkenness, suddenly go: 'Say ... where the hell is Chris?'

The Smash It In Your Facer: There are two categories: the boozer, as in 'I'm off to down ten Jaegermeisters' and then does it; and the person that ends up snogging another person – or people – in a dark corner all evening. The categories often overlap.

The Saturday Night Fever: Alcohol makes this person think they can dance as well as a black person. But they can't. They do the Macarena, or the Electric Slide, or the Running Man. Badly. Potential Saturday Night Fevers have no coordination, and they always scream 'This is my song!' and rush off to wow the crowds in the centre of a circle. I fit into this category.

The Sentimentalist: 'I love you. You promise to be godmother to my children?' This person hugs their friends (and anyone else passing by) compulsively. Often the ritual ends with tears, hugs and more 'You're just my best friend ever.'

The Fighty Couple: They argue about something they don't remember about the next day – like innocent flirting, or her flashing her tits, or him not remembering her mother's second name.

The Lovey-Dovey Face Suckers: Couples that might as well not go clubbing, because they're attached to each other the whole night and get stuck in as though nobody else is actually there.

The Let's Do Something Crazeeeeee: This person will do something like drive their car into the bushes after exiting the club, take all their clothes off and streak in public, or steal road signs and traffic cones because they think it will be funny.

The Please Take Me Home: Your mate isn't having as swell a time as you, or vice versa. She's seen her ex-boyfriend and is whining in your ear about it. Or you've seen your ex-boyfriend snog someone and all you want to do is go home and wail into your pillow. Or everyone else is pissed and you're not. Waiting to be taken home is as shitty as having a mate want you to take her home.

The Messy: This is the person who vomits on the bar counter, drools beer all over themselves, slurs incomprehensibly, passes out under a speaker cradling a bottle of cane, or they're throwing their name all over the place – but not in a funny way.

The No But Of Course I Can: They're so pissed, they leopard crawl to their cars and still insist they can drive even though they can't find the keyhole. Usually an argument ensues, where someone tries to get hold of their keys, followed by 'Fuck off,

I'm perfectly fine for godsh shake. I only had shix drinksh! A sharp slap or another drink to make them pass out sorts out the problem.

The Nap Overer: You only know once you get the phone call the next day.
'Shit fuck shit. I slept over at Clifford's place. Again!'
Or 'Do you remember the name of the guy sleeping next to me?'
Or 'How do I get out of here without waking him up?'
Or 'I met the most incredible oke last night, fuck I wonder if he's going to phone me? Do you think he will? Why hasn't he phoned me yet?'

CLOSURE

I still haven't seen Randy since we broke up. It's been way over eighty days, about a hundred and twenty now, in fact. I still wonder whether Randy is moping without me at all. Certainly not for this long, if he ever did. Deciding not to see him was a good decision. Imagine those poor sods that have office flings and then have to see each other day in, day out? Cutting him out has definitely been the easiest way to move forwards. This staying-friends-after-breaking-up thing isn't feasible. Thank goodness at least I had the sensibility to realise this straight away.

Just as I was pondering all this, something extraordinary happened. He arrived on my doorstep. Just like that. I couldn't believe it; it felt surreal, as if it all happened in slow motion.
Typing on keyboard.
Quiet Sunday afternoon.
Minding my own business.
Movie on low volume in background.
Door phone rings.
Pick up.

You're shitting me.

Heart starts beating at a rate of knots.

Can't stop shaking.

He's walking towards my door.

Fuck. I don't have concealer on.

My hair is a nest.

Open door.

Run into Giulia's room and have mini panic attack.

Walk back to door, as calmly as possible.

Greet each other.

Make small talk.

Fetch his CD from my room.

Shaking.

He follows me into my room.

Bed unmade.

Dildo on side table.

Clothes and shoes everywhere.

Let him out.

Lock gate.

Iron bars between us.

He stops.

Asks if I think he made the right decision.

How am I supposed to know?

'Probably, yes.'

(Actually you made the wrong decision.)

I still love him.

Back to the small talk.

Steel bars.

Silence.

Only Mrs Abdul's birds chirping rather loudly in the passage.

Both just stand, staring ahead.

Unlock gate.

Let him back in.

Sit in lounge.

Movie (period drama) still on in background.

Make tea. On my suggestion.

Forget how he takes his cuppa. (Two sugars.)

Shaking. Calming down.

Small talk.

Am nonchalant. Show no emotion, don't say much.

Am stronger than I think.

Am also dead inside.

Hurt and anger move beneath the deadness with heavy pressure.

Walk to door.

Usher him out.

'Well, have a nice life.'

Lock gate.

Panic.

Walk outside.

He hasn't driven away yet.

Enter gate.

Lock it.

Re-hang the Liechtenstein posters I ordered off the Internet.

Can't find the fucking Prestik.

I don't cry.

Make tea. (Rooibos.)

Sadness. Am empty.

It's finally over.

There's no reason to ever see him again.

Randy and I have closure. I feel sick. But also a strange sense of re-lief. I wonder if he noticed the confident couldn't-care-less woman that I'm trying so hard to be. I didn't show one iota of emotion. I didn't feel too much emotion either. This is excellent news!

GIRLS' STITCH 'N BITCH CLUB

Last night Helen and Lizzy came over to join Giulia and I to commiserate over the state of our lives. I grabbed a pair of knitting needles, a bottle of wine and we sat spread eagled on the floor. The Stitch 'n Bitch Club.

Helen got burgled on Sunday, they cleaned out her closets too – a harsh reality in this town – and as a result is in the throes of a wardrobe crisis. Lizzy is still dealing with her emotional meltdown in front of Gary, and Giulia, well Giulia has no issues as such (Hendrik is a fantastic boyfriend), except she pulled a glute while jogging, and she just likes to listen. Lizzy lay on my bed weeping uncontrollably, and drank most of my wine. As she was leaving she vomited on the pavement outside.

'I think ... I'm dying.'

'Yes, for now you are. Give it a week, you'll be alright. I personally guarantee it.'

'No, really I think I'm dying.'

'There there, it's going to be alright.'

'No really ... I'm choking on a chicken wing. Help me!'

I administered a vigorous back rub and she promptly spat out the offending bone.

She'll pick up the pieces of her busted ego, shattered heart and the remaining threads of her severely wounded dignity, and slowly begin to piece them all back together. I didn't realise she still loved Gary so much.

From: helen@choppersinc.com
To: peasontoast@gmail.com
Subject: clothes and smokes

I bought some Diesel shades. That's the extent of my wardrobe right now, together with your purple dress that smells like how a really smelly thing should smell. I also think I smoked myself retarded last night. Need to stop buying Camel Lights to finance the sale Morgan is having this weekend.

From: elizabeth@downtoearth.com
To: peasontoast@gmail.com
Subject: I have found myself with barnacle

Remember that oke from the weekend who still thinks I'm his girlfriend? I got a dinner invite. Help. I know I smooched him, but since when does he want a girlfriend with baggage? Ah, I suppose that happened to you too, so it's not out of the question. I'm so over men. And I'm so glad you're over them too. Misery loves company, right?

PEAS AND SPINSTERHOOD

Even though I've come a long way since Randy, I'm still petrified of spending quality alone time, just me and Peas. As in, actually spend a night at home, not worrying what everyone else is doing. I'm obviously not quite as independent as I want to be yet. I'm scared to go there. I'm not sure I'm ready to address all my complexities just yet. My biggest fear is being a spinster for the rest of my life and owning a formidable amount of furry creatures. I wasn't so afraid of this after Anthony and I split, but now, after Randy, I fear I will never find anyone ever again. I am damaged goods.

Of late, I've picked up this annoying habit of coming home *toute seule* – alone – and phoning everyone I know either right then or first thing in the morning. The concept of spending an entire day on my own without talking to anyone else is overwhelming. On this particular day which stretched out before me, I called Giulia.

'Where are you? Your flatmate is lonely!'

'I'm sleeping over at Hendrik's house. Why aren't you sleeping like the rest of South Africa?'

Then Lizzy, who I'll probably end up spending the evening with:

'Hi, where are you?'

'On the way home, dude.'

'Oh. Wanna go shopping or something?'

'It's 5:30 a.m. We just got back from a party! Are you still drunk?'

I tried Bennet, but it went straight to voicemail, so as a last resort, I tried Connor who is in New York with Gwendolyn:

'Hi Connor. Whatcha doing?'

'It's 3:30 a.m. Are you in trouble?'

'No .... just wanted to know if you'd like to come round for a cuppa tea when you get back.'

'Jeez. You almost gave me a heart attack. You're lucky Gwendolyn is sleeping on the couch tonight, we broke up again.'

'What's the reason this time?'

'She drinks an exorbitant amount of bottled water. Wherever we go, she carts along a case of bloody Perrier with her, and I finally lost it.'

'Well, at least she's healthy; I've been drinking Jaegermeister all night.'

'It's me or the bottled water. I've given her twenty-four hours to think about it.'

'Right. See you when you get back. I can't believe I just phoned New York.'

'Yeah, and I just paid for it since you called me on my cell phone.'

Next, I phoned my Dad although I knew it was kind of pointless.

'You need to post yourself onto a dating website, Peas. It's the answer.'

'Gee, thanks.'

'It's worked for me. I mean, I go on a date every day of the week,

Peas. Do it, I'm telling you, just do it. Now's not the time to be proud.'

'Goodnight, Dad.'

I thought about calling my mother, but I was certain she'd nag about my decrepit and alcohol-filled existence if she wasn't attending one of her 'silent retreats' at an Ashram, so I instead made one final, desperate call:

'Hi Anthony. How you doing? Want to do coffee sometime?'

'Peas, this isn't a good time. If. You. Know. What. I. Mean.'

'Great. No problem. Forget it.'

So this is the point where I'm meant to sit down by myself and deal with my hang-ups honestly and constructively, right? The simple solution would be to switch off my phone, not go out and get drunk, and focus on why I am petrified of not being liked, loved, why I need a man the whole time, and why I get so angry when one can't commit to me. I have to do it this weekend; I have to just face myself. If I'm going to progress with this spinsterhood thing, I'll need to be fairly independent.

So on Sunday I took a drive out to the Magaliesberg by myself and even refrained from phoning anyone. Flying solo. And took a few notes, while at a tea garden in the middle of the countryside:

I need to talk to my father. At some point. About his lack of commitment when it comes to anything, how I just can't count on him or talk to him seriously. And how this has affected me.

Spinsterhood is routine-based gardening, tending to animals and fostering hobbies (like knitting, which I am actually rather enjoying).

I have to stop boozing away my troubles. Somehow.

PRETTY, YOU'RE THE BOMB

If I can't control what's going on in my head right now (at least not without tranquilisers), I can at least try and reign in my domicile.

I'm fine with our mismatched, commune-type furniture and the fact that my flat isn't going to appear in *House & Garden*. But, we really have to start cleaning up our act. Giulia wholeheartedly agreed with me. Being a fellow Virgo, she likes tidiness and orderliness as much as I do.

GIULIA: 'We need help. A domestic psychologist.'

PEAS: 'Dude, I need a head psychologist before we get a feng shui person.'

GIULIA: 'No no. That's not what I mean ...'

So Giulia and I got a maid. A domestic worker.

This is not a big deal for most middle- to upper-income South Africans. In many cases, a domestic worker becomes part of the family. But this is a big step for me. I grew up with a maid called Flora, bless her Zulu *muhle isikhathulo*. Since then, any other domestic worker, as far as I was concerned, was not going to cut it. Flora carried me on her back in an old blanket when I was two, gave me a couple of good hidings at eight and delivered hot meals to my riddled-with-angst teenage lair when I was sixteen. She was an integral part of my childhood so, naturally, now the only domestic worker I really want is Flora. But this is logistically impossible, since she's retired and resides in Mphophomeni Township in the Natal Midlands.

However, in all honesty, we had no choice. We had to take action. Our place is always engulfed with stray shoes, dead flowers wilting thirstily in vases, clothes all over chairs, CDs covering the carpet, dishes disguising the sink, an eternal bath ring.

So, against my futile protestations, and downright scepticism, Giulia went and hired someone.

'Can't we find Flora? I'll get her up to Jo'burg and take her shopping. She'll get on something epic with Innocence (Bennet's domestic worker).'

'No, you stubborn shit. We're hiring Pretty. Besides, isn't Flora like eighty years old?'

'Yeah, so?'

The weekend before Pretty started working for us, our unspoken motto became: 'Don't worry about it, Pretty is coming on Monday.' Drop spaghetti on the floor? Oh, just leave it. Overflowing ashtray? No problem. No clean crockery? We can use Tupperware. No fresh underwear? Go Scottish Highlander to work. For through the murky haze and build up of sacramental scum in our flat, lies a solution. And her name is Pretty.

Well, all day on Monday I sat at work biting my nails, wondering whether this stranger would clean us out (figuratively) by the time the day was over, and if she'd eat my spinach quiche sitting in the fridge. I roared home, jumping red lights, to find out whether my quiche had been devoured and if my jewellery had disappeared – she was a perfect stranger after all – to find heaven on earth.

The smell of Pine Domestos hit me like a welcome slap to the face. The carpets were spotless. She'd even turned down my sheets. I saw the sink for the first time in months. Underneath the dirt, it appeared that the bath was moulded from pure, white enamel. And my quiche was still intact. Ecstatically, I raced around the flat, which was now what could only be described as a perfectly scrubbed masterpiece. Pretty had worked her backside off. And now I love her. Can't find where she put my Clinique soap, but nevertheless, I love her.

Then, suddenly, my reverie was interrupted by Diego, who was visiting. He lit up a smoke.

GIULIA: 'You're lighting a smoke in this new flat?'

DIEGO: 'We've been smoking here all evening.'

GIULIA: 'Go and smoke outside!'

DIEGO: 'Fuck that, dude, this is not *that* kind of house.'

GIULIA: 'Now it is.'

DIEGO: 'Fine. I'll hang car fresheners around the couch.'

GIULIA: 'Stub it out or I won't serve you any spaghetti.'

PEAS: 'You made spaghetti?'

DIEGO: 'Since when did you become so bossy, mother of Amor Vittone?'

GIULIA: (Gasps indignantly.) 'Since you became an irritating fuckwit.'

DIEGO: 'I'm not a fuckwit.'

GIULIA: 'Oh yes you are. Peas back me up on this.'

PEAS: 'Um ... I don't really ...'

DIEGO: 'I'm *not* a fuckwit.'

He stormed out. Then returned later with a bunny chow from Bismillah in Fordsburg as a peace offering. We ate in silence. And nobody smoked.

INTER-SHAGGING

I haven't panicked much about being on my own lately, although I almost called Lizzy to share my latest revelation with her: people in Jozi, in their mid-twenties, inter-shag. It probably happens in other cities too, but it's particularly prolific here. That's another problem with hooking up with 'random strangers' here. Somehow it always comes back to haunt you. Lizzy is a case in point.

Here's a classic story of incest that you don't hear everyday – it has to be one of the most spectacular examples of inter-shagging to date. Definitely one for the grandkids.

Diego used to go out with Pedra (pronounced Pay-dra. *Very important*). Pedra used to date George, who used to date Veronica. Now Diego is seeing Veronica. They've all practically slept with each other. They're dating each other's exes without even blinking an eye. Exes going out with exes who are exes. Have you ever?

Sweet Lord above, am I living in Blikkiesfontein? Is the ten-million-strong city in which I currently reside a Platteland town?

Really, it's not like the ten inhabitants of Hekville who are forced to have sex with each other because there's no one else around.

Giulia and I pondered the ridiculousness of the situation over Woolies Zesty Italian chardonnay at home. The only logical conclusion we arrived at is that people go for the same types of people. Perhaps George and Diego like the same eyes. Or their new partners wear similar shoes. Or uncannily both flounce around in gypsy skirts and laugh hysterically at *Southpark*. Perhaps it's time to move away from Jo'burg. This town just isn't big enough for everyone anymore.

Out of sheer frustration that the Jo'burg pond seems to be getting smaller and smaller, I indulged in a boozy midweek lunch at Wandies in Soweto today on whose communal graffiti wall I scrawled my name. Then, it was off to the Zoo Lake Bowling Club where gin and tonics go for R8,50 and scholarly teenagers flock around for cheap beer and cheap kisses. So much for promising myself to slow down. My mates and I proceeded to meet two hilarious men by the names of Sexypants and Cute Asssssssss. (Yes, with that many 's's.)

After many a drink was bought and drunk, and conversation had flowed like the River Severn during the Welsh flood of 1978, I managed to reverse my car up an embankment on two wheels. The right back wheel and left front wheel.

How was I to know that there was a jutting out tow thingie under my back bumper that would drill its way into the grassy knoll on which I had unwittingly reversed? This was especially embarrassing since Sexypants and Cute Asssssssss witnessed the whole thing from the parking lot while 'When I dip, you dip, we dip ... if you ain't dippin', you must be trippin' ...' was playing loudly on my CD player as I roared up the hill backwards, wheels a-spinning in mid-air. The whole drunken evening I had charmed them with my rapier wit, only to go and park my vehicle halfway backwards up a fifty-five degree bowling green slope.

I seem to be making a national pastime out of embarrassing myself in front of hot men lately. Pete, a cutie I met at Manhattan a few weeks ago, came up say hello to me. He tapped me on the shoulder; I turned around and for two seconds (one Mississippi, two Mississippi) couldn't for the life of me remember who he was. Odd, since he's the fellow I've been masturbating over for the last few days. The only explanation I can find for getting so mislaid midweek at the Bowling Club is well, I had spent the whole day in Soweto researching stories to write about ethnic African cuisine. And I did this while ushering around a tour group because it was The Sub's idea to start Good Food Tours Around Townships, and I've been left with the job of escorting Brits from deepest darkest Surrey around places like Soweto. (Do I look like David Attenborough? I'm a journalist for Christ's sake.)

Now my car looks like I reversed it up an especially large pile of bovine manure. Sulking, I pulled into the Engen garage, bought myself three strawberry milkshakes and a *heat* magazine, and then realised I'd left the Bowling Club without saying cheerio to Man I Met At The Bar, but then, perhaps I'll retain an air of mystery. Perhaps he even wondered where I'd disappeared to.

By the way, the car-guard's eyes were on stalks. Who knew a twolitre Beetle could take it up the ass?

ANCESTRAL DEBATE

Diego came round to tell us how wonderful his new girlfriend Veronica is. 'New girlfriend' is a loaded term, since there's nothing new about her amongst close, inter-shagging circles, is there?

We ended up having a heated debate about our ancestry, which I suppose is inevitable when you put an Italian person, a Portuguese person and a half-French person in a room together. This merging of three cultures occurs on an almost daily basis in our lounge. Why we're so adamantly loyal to our roots is beyond me, since we're all as South African as boerewors.

DIEGO: 'Oy, Charles de Gaulle, pass me the ashtray.'

PEAS: 'Easy, Vasco da Gama.'

DIEGO: 'If it weren't for Vasco, Mozambique wouldn't be here today.'

PEAS: 'Vasco destroyed the entire country! Along with Angola!'

DIEGO: 'Well, let's not go into what the French did when they colonised themselves around the world.'

PEAS: 'We might've colonised, but we didn't kill millions of people.'

DIEGO: 'And what about slavery in the Deep South?'

PEAS: 'What about it? At least we have great cuisine! You don't hear anybody saying, "Hmmm, I could really do with an espetada right now."'

DIEGO: 'Is that garlic I smell, Edith Piaf?'

PEAS: 'Well, Lourenco Marques, at least our national food isn't a piece of meat wedged between two buns. At least we have wine, cheese and *Confi du canard.*'

DIEGO: 'Ever heard of Nando's?'

PEAS: 'I suppose they have Nando's in Portugal do they?'

DIEGO: 'At least we weren't taken in two world wars.'

PEAS: 'We're lovers not fighters, Bartholomew Dias. You won't hear anybody saying "Wow, Portuguese lovers are the best in the world." You may hear that French people are great in the sack, though.'

DIEGO: 'So they're great in the sack, so what?'

PEAS: 'And you won't hear people saying, "Lisbon. Hmmm. More romantic than Paris. Better food."'

DIEGO: 'At least when I speak English in Lisbon people respond to me! Rude fucking Frenchies.'

PEAS: 'Hey, fuck you.'

DIEGO: 'Fuck you! You guys need to learn to speak English!'

PEAS: 'Why should we?'

DIEGO: 'Because, you fucking well should. Now, fuck you.'

PEAS: 'Yeah, well fuck you. *Va te faire enculer!*'

DIEGO: 'What does that mean?'

PEAS: '"Why don't you go and fuck yourself." That's what it means.'

We sulked for ten minutes and then decided to leave it. Giulia then went on about how pasta has been bastardised around the rest of the Western world and how they just don't make it like her Ton Ton used to. Yes, a volatile Italian flying off the handle is exactly what was needed to diffuse the Porra-Francophile thing.

GIULIA: 'Shut up, both of you! How would you feel if your grand-parents were bought out by Fattis & Monis?'

PEAS: 'What's wrong with Fattis & Monis? I saw you using it the other day.'

GIULIA: 'It's not made from durum wheat! Me, use Fattis & Monis? Have you been smoking your socks?'

PEAS: 'Dude, I saw you take the box out of the cupboard and pour that very spaghetti in a pot on the stove.'

GIULIA: 'Lies, Peas. I'd never do such a thing.'

DIEGO: 'Dude, I saw that too.'

GIULIA: 'I'm most upset that both of you would think I'd do such a thing.'

PEAS: 'There there. I won't tell anybody, your secret is safe with me.'

I could murder a camembert *au coulis fraise*.

Feeling off kilter, I decided to call Connor, who is back from New York *sans* Gwendolyn. It appears that the bottled water break up is ongoing. (Bottlegate? Although he insists that if she cuts back on her Perrier intake, he may take her back.)

I met him at Zoo Lake, where we strolled, ate ice creams and threw crumbs at the ducks. Our afternoon was interrupted by a call from Gwendolyn to vow to Connor that she would stop drinking Perrier for a while. He replied, 'That's nice. I'm busy. See you later.' I'm impressed by his resilience to not go running back. There must be something more to it than just bottled water but he's not telling me what.

God I'm lonely. I'm terrified of the future. Will I be single forever? I can't wait to drink again. Detox is overrated; it suddenly gives me all this time to think.

CHAPTER NINE

THE BOOGIE THAT BE

I've managed to stay away from alcohol for almost a week now; surely that's enough? I'm proud of myself and feeling good. Bored, but good. And as such, I have turned to music.

Many times I've been told that I need to reassess my music collection. I used to care and take offence when others criticised my eclectic taste but it's not my fault no-one else listens to Dionne Warwick's *Greatest Hits*, Burt Bacharach or Lionel Richie. And it's not my concern that nobody appreciates the rhythms of Petula Clarke or Take That. I own the entire Monster Hits collection dating back to 1991, and I bloody well like it. Especially when it's karaoke hour in Illovo.

Okay, maybe it's a little off.

My musical taste is fundamentally diverse. The Bee Gees sits next to Limp Bizkit, Metallica sits next to Mike & the Mechanics and Dr Dre is next to *Bump 2*. However, last night, I sat down to my boys of the Stone Age. Verdi's *La Traviata*, Bach's *Brandenburg Concerto*, and Andrea Bocelli's *Liberta*, and wondered how on earth somebody could not appreciate the allegro and staccato of classical music. While I'm detoxing my body, classical music is perfect to detox the mind.

Much of my other music is toaster-in-the-bath cheesy puffery that leaves one feeling less than exquisite, especially since every Lionel Richie lyric seems to describe my trivial little existence.

('Say you, say me ... as we go down that lonesome highway ... seems the hardest thing to do ... is to find a friend or two ... that helping hand, someone who understands ...')

All my music reminds me of someone or some place. Classical music immediately clears my mind and makes me think of snow-capped European hilltops, antique harpsichords, ballet dresses and my grandmother's ratatouille. Light, fluffy, peripheral stuff.

Mozart was a tortured prodigy who listened to the same piece of music over and over again. He also drank away his life savings, partied with harems of women and danced on piano tops. If I lived in Vienna during the 1800s, I'm certain we would've gotten along like a house on fire. He sounds like a riot.

Beethoven is another story. I played large quantities of his sonatas when I practiced the piano religiously. However, he must have suffered some sort of mental psychosis considering his father bashed him around the ears every night in a drunken rage. (Alcohol seems to be a common factor in these composite success stories.)

But, and let's pretend he wasn't the gay equivalent of David Furnish, Tchaikovsky is someone I definitely would have bedded. Even if it meant I had to move to St Petersburg, live in a gulag and queue for bread. His music is exceptional. I'm certain he must have had a sense of humour as well, if you consider his *Symphony No. 6*. It's pompous, but cheekily so. Aah ... the romanticism of *The Nutcracker Suite*. There's a party in my pants, Tchaikovsky, and you're totally invited.

CHANGE

I've come to the conclusion that change is the only constant in life. And whether it's for the best or not, it's difficult. Especially when the change involves one's best friend.

CONNOR: 'Peas, I have some news. You'd better sit down.'

PEAS: 'Let me guess, bottled water is a thing of the past and you and Gwynnie are back together.'

CONNOR: 'Well, yes ... and I've also been offered an expat position overseas.'

PEAS: 'I'm sorry, what?'

CONNOR: 'Do you want to fetch yourself a cup of soothing herbal tea first?'

PEAS: 'Dammit, no, tell me now, what is going on? Where are you going? Why?'

CONNOR: 'The company has offered to send me to India. And Gwendolyn wants to come with me.'

PEAS: 'I feel sick. When did this happen?'

CONNOR: 'About ten minutes ago. You're the first person I've told.'

PEAS: 'Actually, I'm the second person you've told. Gwendolyn was the first. How long are you going for? I didn't realise you and Gwendolyn were that serious. I mean, let's be honest, you've had a rather rocky relationship until now! Is this really a good idea?'

CONNOR: 'I'm going for a year. She thinks this would be a whole new start for us. A new beginning. Maybe she's right? I don't know; it's worth a try I suppose.'

PEAS: 'Are you being serious? I can't believe this. You're leaving.'

CONNOR: 'Next week. Which means we have seven days to jam-pack our diaries with Peas-Connor time, okay?'

PEAS: 'I'm in shock.'

Gwendolyn is going with him. Well, she wasn't when they broke up in a coffee shop the day before, but she's going with him now. I can't believe he's actually going. And with his on-off girlfriend in tow.

I'm a little cut up, to say the least.

On Saturday, I went to Connor's impromptu farewell party. Being the insatiable exhibitionist that he is, he got naked and danced round the house, willy a-swinging. He often strips when he gets trashed. Gwendolyn had all of her twittering cronies around her and seemed awfully pleased with herself. I, however, wasn't all jolly hockey sticks, and remained sober. I was afraid that if I drank I'd fly off the handle.

The day of his departure is imminent. Gwendolyn is running around with a huge smile on her face. It's fairly obvious how happy she is to be whisking my best friend away from me to an exotic and far-off destination. I'm not certain if Connor really feels the same way – despite his drunken performance at his party, I sensed that, beneath the happy face, he was perplexed, as if it was all happening to someone else. Meanwhile, I'm completely overwhelmed. How did this just happen overnight? He's leaving. He's really leaving.

BYE CONNOR

I've been crying all morning. I never really thought this day would come – so much has been going on, the future always seemed just out of reality's grasp. Gwendolyn is right by his side, on seat 16C, to be exact. How is it that even though this relationship seems so dysfunctional and, quite frankly, odd, *they* are moving to a foreign country together for a year? Yet, what appears to have been a fairly normal relationship – mine – fell apart for good. That aside, I mustn't be selfish. He's embarking on a new adventure and I will be happy for him. Them. But hell, I'm going to miss him so much.

How is this crazy city going to be bearable without Connor? Who will I talk to about if black holes really exist and whether Stephen Hawking is just a conspiracy theorist? I've been compiling some highlights to remember Connor by:

- Chatting about relationships, art and being hippies while puffing away on Rafiki, the Tanzanian pipe.
- Dressing up for the River Club Golf Club, hanging onto his and Bennet's arms and pretending that I was their cherry.

- Him bringing me a tramezzini after I left work early, crying over a man.
- Pizza and vodka regulars at Trabella.
- Hanging his red doondies on the pole outside Jolly Roger – and watching them sway in the breeze over 4th Avenue for five weeks before management took them down.
- Lusitoland, caipirinhas, Vegas showgirl outfits and him wearing my bra.
- Visiting the Herbert Baker museum together.
- Me squeezing his nipple through his torn shirt at the Songwriters' Club, in Newtown, the first time we met, then subsequently realising we were both studying at UCT anyway.
- Drinking gin and tonics in his parent's garden under the mosaic. Him dropping his pants while golfing on the lawn, for our supposed benefit.
- Him dropping his pants at every drunken social occasion, period.
- Sitting around bonfires on the beach in Plett.
- Him attending tennis braais dressed like Bjorn Borg.
- Him phoning my mum to reassure her that I'm a 'nice young lady'.
- Us taking photos at the base of Ponte Tower at 9:00 p.m. on a Sunday night, when we were doing a photography course together.
- Eating Kung Fu Kitchen noodles and watching *Southpark* on nights in.
- Fraternising with the Rothbergs.
- Halloween party at the Colony Arms. Connor dressing up as Frikkie van der Veldskoen with a mullet, tiny nut-cracker shorts and a comb in his socks. (And he still got lucky. Twice.)
- Midnight phone calls, where I can't understand a word of his voice message the next morning, and vice versa.
- Calling Randy anything but his real name for the entire duration

of our relationship. ('How are things going with Andrew?' 'Randy, Connor.' 'Peas, John is hilarious.')

- Driving past Parkhurst's George's on 4th, pumping Punjabi MC, windows down, bass in our face, and patrons recoiling in horror.
- Giulia and I giving him a ballet and gymnastics show in his room after too many doubles at the Jolly.

I took him to the airport. Gwen went with her parents and met us there. I don't think she appreciated me and him having some last time together before the final farewell. Who knows when I will ever see him again? During the journey, Connor then raised something that we've never discussed, 'Why, when we were both single in the past, didn't we ever break our friendship boundary?'

It wasn't something I considered, because we were 'just friends'. And we both agreed that we would never want to ruin that.

Our goodbye was awkward and stiff and I don't understand why. I tried to pretend how happy I was for him, and that I was okay with being left in boring, heartbreaking old Jo'burg. I couldn't hug him, because then I'd cry so I gave him a kiss and left as soon as he'd checked in, no waving through the barriers and all that drawn-out stuff. Gwendolyn was with her family, but I noticed her watching Connor and me saying our goodbyes from the corner of her beady little eye. I hope he doesn't return in tie-dye and a turban.

Of course he's going to miss our incestuous little circle, not to mention me, Peas a la Incredible. Right? A sad day indeed.

The conversation in the car has planted a little seed of regret of not ever having explored a romantic relationship. Why had Connor waited until now to bring this up? He couldn't have mentioned it at a worse time than minutes before he was leaving to go and live in a foreign country thousands of kilometres away.

Why is life so full of loss?

PICK-UP LINES

I need to meet more men to try and fill this void. But, unless I join a squash club or something – hell no – I'm going to have to do it the only way I know how: nightclubs, booze and pick-up lines. Since being single, I've been on the receiving end of some real beauties.

Here are some of the lines I've been subjected to roughly in the space of three months, all uttered in seriousness:

- Those are *seriously funky* reading glasses. (Oh dear. I don't wear reading glasses.)
- Didn't mean to offend you about the glasses thing. (Really. It's all right.)
- Hello beautiful. (Hello Donald Trump.)
- You have this look about you ... you know ... this wall. Like I can't get in. (You would be right there.)
- Hey, check, your shoes have a picture of Michael Jackson on them! (Huh?) And he's staring up your skirt! (Huh?)
- So, now that you're single ... (Yes?)
- Wanna fuck? (Oh yes please, you sweet-talking bastard.)
- Wanna go spinning with me? (This has been asked four times over e-mail, the phone and SMS. My answer? I equate spinning with hell.) He then proceeded to tell me how wonderful, amazing, incredible his girlfriend is. (Here's a free idea: take *her* spinning, idiot.)
- So ... why do people call you Peas on Toast? ('Cos ... er ... that's my name.)
- Why on earth would Randy dump you? (Because he's retarded? Perhaps you can tell me)
- Your jacuzzi party last year was wild. Can we do it again? Next time I'm sitting next to you. (Who are you? Why were you at my jacuzzi party?)

It all makes me really miss having a boyfriend. Careful what you wish for though, because I seemed to have found one. It's barnacled itself to me – and it's name, if you can believe it, is Randy. How many Randys can there be in this world? Two maybe? I met him at Manhattan and he used one of these apt pick up lines on me. I gave in – he wasn't a bad-looking chap – and handed him my number. We even snogged. Last night he SMSed me to ask me to dinner. And just seeing the 'From: New Randy' on my telephone makes me feel a little pukey.

The panic is setting in. Not because he isn't nice, not because he's the first guy I've given my number to in months but because he has the same name as Randy. It's just a little, well, weird. And I don't know his surname, so I can't even call him Jones or Smith as an alternative. I don't think I'll take this further, more for his sake than mine.

Giulia had some upfront, no-nonsense advice:

'Kiss him, dance with him, then dump him. It worked for me when I met Other Roland after the ex-Roland broke up with me.'

'Yes, but I'm unsure whether I can even do that.'

'Close your eyes, have a drink. You'll be fine.'

'Sometimes I really wish I could be you and you could be me.'

CHAPTER TEN

I made a chart last night. The chart of change. Mum told me it's not about perfection but rather progress, and that I should embrace my 'life journey'. Unfortunately I expect perfection from myself and the others around me. I expect them to live up to my standards and if they don't, I'm extremely disappointed and I start to resent them.

So I made a list. I need goals, I can't live day to day like all those happy-go-lucky enlightened ones out there without something to work towards. This is what I came up with:

OLD PEAS: Oh, yes I know how that feels, it's happened to me too.

New PEAS: That's really shit. Tell me what happened. I've leaned on you, now lean on me.

OLD PEAS: The world has come to an end. I got dumped.

New PEAS: The world has come to an end. I got dumped. Can I cry and rant about this for a week? Then I promise to start dealing with it.

OLD PEAS: Let's go out and get drunk. It'll numb the pain.

New PEAS: Let's go out and get drunk, only because we're celebrating something, not because we've had a bad week or the bastard cheated on you/me.

OLD PEAS: Break up. Hook up. Fuck up. Cover up.

New PEAS: Break up. Be alone for a while. Learn from the mistake. Face up. Let Lizzy give me straight-up advice without getting defensive.

OLD PEAS: Over exaggerate and exacerbate problem with continuous woe-is-me attitude, and spiral into an all-encompassing depression.

NEW PEAS: I refuse to be my own worst enemy. Look at what there is to be grateful for – a career, a roof over my head, friends and two healthy parents.

OLD PEAS: The guy will leave me because I'm too difficult.

NEW PEAS: If he leaves, I can be by myself. I am a strong, independent woman who can survive heartbreak. (Maybe with tranquilisers but hey, everyone's fallible.)

OLD PEAS: Writes long change charts that she never looks at again.

NEW PEAS: Actually applies what she writes.

OLD PEAS: Has to live up to everyone's (including my own) expectations of being a fun, crazy, party animal.

NEW PEAS: I am allowed to be sad.

OLD PEAS: Stuffs the root of the problem to the back of the brain and lets it manifest through projections.

NEW PEAS: (What does that even mean? That was Lizzy's input. She's a Psych. Masters major.)

Will approach her father for closure and answers and will strive to release hang-ups. (What?)

Lizzy thinks a lot of what's going on with me right now has to do with my dad. My dad who doesn't even live in Jo'burg who is living his life exactly the way he intended. How should that affect me?

'That's precisely it, Peas. I think your dad is reliving a childhood, and hasn't been there for you during yours. I think you need to address some stuff with him. Maybe you two need a heart to heart?'

Should I even delve into the patriarchal abyss? I'm not entirely certain. Besides, how could what happened way back when affect my relationships now? 'Well, he did have an affair and run off with his mistress,' offered Lizzie helpfully. She shouldn't be a business analyst, she should be a shrink.

Either way, I have a lot to think about.

Meanwhile I'm missing Connor terribly. He phoned me last night. Gwendolyn met an Arab oil sheik while they were out and about in Delhi and, packed up and headed to Sharm El Sheik with him:

CONNOR: 'She told me this guy has a thing for nether moles and that she needed to "experiment with other ethnic groups".'

PEAS: 'That's pants. Seriously?'

CONNOR: 'Yup.'

PEAS: 'You alright?'

CONNOR: 'Yes. Kind of.'

PEAS: 'You sure? I miss you.'

CONNOR: 'I miss you too.'

PEAS: 'So she just upped and went?'

CONNOR: 'Just like that. So much for "new beginnings". I'm almost relieved though. I mean, if she doesn't like India or me, it's better that I know now, not months down the line.'

PEAS: 'What actually happened?'

CONNOR: 'She was shopping somewhere – possibly for bottled water – and disappeared. I couldn't get hold of her. Next thing, she sweeps in through the front door wearing a kaffiya head scarf and says she's made a big mistake and has finally met someone who appreciates the real her. Whatever that means.'

PEAS: 'Oh cripes.'

CONNOR: 'I didn't even try and convince her to stay. Helped her pack her bags, and off she went.'

PEAS: 'Perhaps it's for the best.'

CONNOR: 'Quite. She was beginning to get on my nerves anyway.'

I'm certain that the wench will go grovelling back to him when the novelty fades and I sure as hell hope he doesn't take her back.

I decided to follow Lizzy's advice last week. Well, not entirely. I penned my father a letter – it came from a raw and horrible place. I'm not even sure if I'll ever send it. When I told Mum, she said that the process of writing it would be healing and if I liked she would come over and burn it with me in the communal garden, and then sprinkle the ashes on her bougainvillea.

Dear Dad,

A few things have happened recently that have kick-started me into action. There's no structure to this letter. It's been nine years since you left Mum. I know you were going through your mid-life crisis, and I know you were infatuated with the woman you ran off with but it felt as if you left me as well as her. I know I'm a lot like you when it comes to being impulsive and intense.

There's one thing from your abandonment of Mum/us that has manifested into something huge that I urgently need to address. But upfront let me reassure you that I appreciate and value the way I was brought up, educated, disciplined and loved as a child.

You seemed to have a happy marriage for the better part of twenty-three years. You and Mum are both highly strung individuals, so as far as the gene pool goes, I can't really escape that. There are some positives to being this way – it fuels my creativity, it makes me analytical and I'm constantly seeking ways to escape my comfort zone. Sometimes with terrible results. The anxiety it brings me, however, is not cool. But that's another conversation – mainly for the shrink I think I might start seeing next week.

Maybe it's delayed grief, post-traumatic stress disorder, or whatever the Freuds out there may call it, but your abandoning Mum has fucked up any trust I have, in anyone really, even myself. I saw Mum break into millions of fragments and I had to pick up the pieces. You were in love with her and vowed to be with her forever but then you walked away with what seemed like complete indifference. Or at least it looked that way to me.

I know there are always two sides to a story but it's made my confidence in men, and largely in the human race, null and void. I'm not blaming you, Dad, but I need to tell you these things so that you know how they affected me.

And still, after all these years, you can't be an adult. You never listen to what I have to say, you're too busy living your rockstar dream, flying planes around, being reckless and crazy, and I feel desperately in need of your attention and love. I'm beginning to think that this is why I always need a boyfriend's approval. Someone to love me. The point? Maybe if you listened to me, I wouldn't need so much reassurance from other men. I might not be so needy or feel like a failure when people are disappointed in me. You haven't been there for me for so long in any real way that I clutch onto anything – friends, a boyfriend, alcohol – for security and comfort. And hold on for dear life.

I know this is harsh but it's not said to hurt you. It's to help make sense of my baggage. Now that I'm feeling a new sense of clarity and want to change for the better by breaking destructive patterns, I have to address the anger I feel and somehow let it go. I don't want to be self-obsessed anymore. I need patience and guidance from you, Dad. I need to know that you care for me and love me no matter what.

So these are the changes I'm trying to make, but I want your help and input. And I need to know you're sorry for how you've dealt with things.

I do love you, Dad. Like me, you're an imperfect individual;
you dance to the beat of a different drum and I admire you
for that. Once again, it's not that I blame you fully for any-
thing, it's just that it's affected me more than I ever thought it
would.
Love,
Peas

I sent it. I have no idea how he will react.

Outside my world, other big things are happening. The Frenchies
won the semi-final against Portugal in the World Cup. Diego must
be really angry, he hasn't even come over to look inside our fridge.
Giulia put him on speakerphone when he called to rant, 'I'm not for
a second denying the fact that my team are currently sub-standard
soccer players. But I'm *sorry*. I've had it with you Francophiles rul-
ing the frigging world. First the cheese, then the wine, *ah oui let us*
not forget ze stupeed wine, and then there was ze Va Va Voom ad
campaign, and now this. Fuck this, I'm going out. And you girls –
now finalists in the World Cup – aren't coming with me. Goodbye.'
    If only soccer was the biggest issue in my life right now.

Turns out Dad does check his mail. After two days, he wrote back:

My darling Peas
It saddened me to get your letter, but what the hell are you
talking about? You're a confident girl. Has another guy ripped
your heart out? What do you want me to listen to specifically?
Have I not listened to you? Okay, I'll phone you later. Don't
worry, NOT from the plane. In the meantime, here's a song for

you. It'll make you feel all better.

(He attached an MP3 of Nat King Cole's 'Unforgettable'.)

Lots of love

Dad xx

P.S. Don't judge my behaviour or judge who I am as a person on my mistakes only. But maybe you'll only realise this when you're a lot older and wiser.

Typical. I fought back tears of anger and sadness. Why does he always have to brush important things off? I immediately dialled his number.

'Dad, I'm sick of this. You're never there for me when I need you! You're only surface level. You're volatile, you're all over the place, can I count on you for anything? Have I ever been able to count on you?'

Silence.

'Who's the adult here anyway? While you're flying around the country with no GPS, I'm worried about your safety and, frankly, your state of mind. I am not blaming you entirely for my issues, Dad, but this certainly contributes to them. Call me when you're available and when you can perhaps act like a father.'

I then hung up. And called Lizzy right away. 'You've done the right thing, Peas. It had to come out and I'm proud of you.'

The whole night I tossed and turned, tormented by guilt. I'd obviously really hurt him and I don't ever remember my father being hurt about anything. I don't think he realised I'd react this way. But I'm fed up with his devil-may-care attitude.

First thing in the morning, he called me. In tears. I've never heard my father cry before. Not even after he left my mother that surprisingly hot summer's afternoon the middle of my Matric final exams. 'Peas, I'm so sorry. My affair was never meant to cause so much hurt, and I had no idea you felt this way. I dealt with the situation terribly.

I am sorry I haven't been there for you. I love you so much.'

I burst into tears. 'I just want to be one of those ... (gulp, sob, snot) 'sassy, independent ... women' (gulp, snot, tears) '... who is responsible ... and can ... cope.'

'Peas. Let's go on holiday together. Just you and me. I want to make it up to you, and I want to talk to you. Properly, face to face.'

I said I'd think about it.

SHARM EL SHEIK OR BUST

God it helps when you know that you're not the only twenty something trying to figure things out. Poor Connor. Gwendolyn returned from Sharm El Sheik after just one weekend, just as I suspected she would. Apparently the sheik tried to trade her in for ten camels. Straight back into the arms of Connor, sitting dolefully in Delhi. Except, this time, he didn't take her back.

> From: connor@irishcarbomb.com
> To: peasontoast@gmail.com
> Subject: Sharm was a sham
>
> She came back. She even had the nerve to bring me a present from the desert – a paper maché camel curio that expels a very realistic-sounding 'bwwwwaaaaaa' from its mouth when you press a button. I can use it as an amusing paperweight.
>
> I think I was over Gwendolyn before this all even began. Really, I wanted to believe that we could make a go of it here, but after hours of solitary soul searching in my apartment I realised it wasn't even the mole. Or the fact she drinks litres of bottled water. Or that she thinks my feet smell. Or that we break up every two and a half seconds. I'm not in love with her and never was, and she's not in love with me.
>
> I put her on a plane back home, and feel heaps better. I might

even go down the road for a chicken masala to celebrate. I miss you, mate.

Connor

CHAPTER ELEVEN

So, now that I've come to terms with the fact that I'm actually not as big a screw-up as I thought I was, I'm not doing anything terribly self-destructive (barring my nicotine habit which is back with a vengeance). I'm also feeling a lot more calm and happy. Sorting through the wreckage of your past and facing up to it will do that for you. Even Giulia has noticed a difference in me.

GIULIA: 'Peas, I'm not sure how you're going to take this, but Hendrik and I were thinking of moving in together.'

PEAS: 'Of course you are. That's fantastic!'

GIULIA: 'What, you sure?'

PEAS: 'Of course, it's the natural way things go. When did you both decide?'

GIULIA: 'You don't want to come with us? I asked Hendrik to find a place with a spare room for you.'

PEAS: 'No, no. Don't worry about me, I'll find another housemate.'

GIULIA: 'You're going to *replace me just like that*?'

PEAS: 'You're irreplaceable. But yes, give or take.'

GIULIA: 'What's happened to you? You're all ... stable and understanding.'

PEAS: 'I didn't even notice.'

I still need to make a decision about whether to venture on a holiday with my father. If I do go, I mustn't expect too much, dynamics don't change overnight.

Also, something new has come to light. Since his e-mail, I've had a rather unfamiliar sensation regarding Connor. I know that we're both going through immense changes right now – albeit different circumstances – but there's something strange going on between us. A new vibe. I'm putting time aside to analyse it later.

I really wish he was here to support the French soccer team with me, even if we are the under dogs. France lost the Soccer World Cup to Italy last night. Does he even know they lost? He'd have patted my back, whispered in my ear that all the Italians want is an Oscar and buy me a brie wedge to show his loyalty towards my team. I almost started crying during the nail-biting match. The deal was, if Italy won, I have to make Giulia my salmon á la Va Va Voom. If France won, she has to make me risotto con funghi.

Putain.

And don't think that Diego isn't going on ad nauseam about this either. The man will not shut up. I've buried myself under the duvet and turned off my phone. Giulia is being surprisingly unItalian about it all in front of me, she's gone freakily quiet. Not even an 'I told you so.' Sure, I hear her whooping to her Itye mates about it over the phone, but she simply stares at me in pity when I emerge from my boudoir looking like Brigitte Bardot after being beaten with a ladle of scampi. My grandmére phoned me crying. This is not good news for the French.

Dad left a message on my phone: 'Peas, I'm thinking a lot about what you said. Just know that I love you, my lovely daughter.'

I felt sad.

Later on, Diego coined a theory, once everyone had stopped sulking, about what happened during the World Cup final.

'I know what the Italian player said to Zidane to make him lose his rag.'

'Oh yeah, what?'

'Your mother sucks knob in the slums of Algiers. And then Zidane lost it.'

COCKTAILS, SHMOCKTAILS

I went to a somewhat dull cocktail do last night. Tasty snacks though. I departed after my third glass of wine, because, quite frankly, all the couples were calling each other 'babe' and planting kisses on each other's foreheads. I just wanted to slap all of them and tell them to grow up.

Besides, I have a date tomorrow night. God knows why I've done this to myself. Pete, a man I met a few weeks ago at the Bowling Club (aka Sexy Assssssssss) asked me yesterday to go to dinner tonight – via SMS, mind you. I hate SMS set-ups. All the men in the world, listen up: don't do this. It's a shoddy way of asking a lady on a date. I almost said no, just based on his etiquette, but then figured, what's the big deal? Maybe he'll turn out to be the love of my life. (Although logically I can quite firmly confirm that he is not, based on the few things I know about him.) Then again, New Peas doesn't need to find the love of her life. She'll embark on this date simply because she's free that night, will have fun and will enjoy herself. Mum and Dad both reacted predictably to the news of me dating again.

MUM: 'I'm so pleased. Try not to chase this one away, Peas. I know how intense you can be. Try meditating beforehand to enter a relaxed state of mind, and remember to cleanse your bedroom with your rose quartz.'

PEAS: 'For your information, Mum, I'm not that interested. So before you choose the wedding venue, I'd suggest that rather you don't.'

DAD: 'Peas, I'm flying over Swaziland right now. It's not as scenic as I thought.'

PEAS: 'Dad what have I told you about using your cell while operating an aeroplane? Turn it off. Now.'

DATE

Pardon me for my lack of good demeanour this morning. I got to bed at 3:00 a.m., the world is swimming in front of my eyes and people seem to be talking unbelievably slowly. Plus, after arriving home at that ungodly hour, I found Diego asleep in my bed. (I guess he's forgiven us for not allowing him to smoke inside and for winning the World Cup.) He didn't even fart or try to touch my bottom. (I think it was the Mickey Mouse pyjamas.)

The date with Pete turned out rather well. The reason I got home so late is because *I enjoyed myself*. I didn't try to flee as I've done with other guys over the last five months, nor have I thought beyond the moment to 'I wonder if *he'll* offer to have my babies?' I simply enjoyed his company and, admittedly, the smooching thereafter. We ate lamb shank and spoke about how JFK really died, pineapples, things that are pineapple shaped, pineapple textured and pineapple coloured. He might have bad date-asking etiquette, but the man sure knows how to kiss.

After we were done swapping saliva, I went home. He's a good enough guy, but a nap-over would've been unnecessary. That said, if I'm completely honest with myself, I'm probably going to choose not to see him again. Dating is admin. Games are involved. And I'll only break his heart if I string him along after such a pleasurable night and, believe you me, he doesn't want to be involved with a woman who's still dealing with so much baggage. It was great, I did exactly as I intended. I will not try and prolong it.

EPIPHANY

I've just returned from Manhattan. Lizzy and company hit the vomit pit hard, I held back. Hell, am I sensible or what? And thank goodness I did, for here I am at 2:00 a.m., with a startling clarity that I've never felt in my life. I know how I am going to deal with my demons. It's all come together!

I had a total epiphany: I'd rather being alone than with someone just for the sake of it. The clarity happened to surface on the way back from that cheesy, yet strangely pleasant nightclub after dropping Pete off at his complex. (You guessed it. I was stupid and did see him again.) This is last time I will ever see Pete and it was mainly to bang the final nail into the coffin. We had fun, but I didn't want to deal with him waking up next to me and regretting my decision.

I feel like a hero.

TOASTY

The week's hermitage is over. The digs got together last night for some wine and some Eminem. That being me and Giulia. And of course, Diego. Giulia's letting us smoke inside again.

For some reason, Diego and I couldn't find a lighter to ignite our cigarettes. Hence the conversation:

DIEGO: 'See that's the bitch with suddenly getting a maid – there's no random shit lying all over the place anymore.'

PEAS: 'You sure you don't have a lighter?'

DIEGO: 'Certain.'

PEAS: 'Okay, please won't you fetch the toaster?'

DIEGO: 'You fetch the toaster. Christ, I'm starting to feel like a stranger in my own house.'

PEAS: 'This isn't your house.'

DIEGO: 'Well, is it not my house? Really?'

PEAS: 'No. *Mia casa e* NO *tua casa*, china, now please fetch me the toaster so we can smoke.'

DIEGO: 'Well since it's *your* toaster, you bloody well fetch it.'

PEAS: 'No.'

DIEGO: 'Fine. We'll just sit here then.'

PEAS: 'Fine. I don't need a cigarette anyway.'

DIEGO: 'Neither do I.'

PEAS: 'Good. 'Cos I'm not fetching the toaster.'

DIEGO: 'Excellent. I can sit here all night.'

PEAS: 'Despite the quality of company, I'm perfectly comfortable. And it feels great not to smoke. Great.'

DIEGO: '*Will you please, please* fetch it.'

PEAS: 'You fetch it, for crying in a bucket!'

DIEGO: 'Fuck you.'

PEAS: 'Fuck you and fuck the toaster.'

Giulia arrived home to find us sipping on our wine and sulking into our glasses and was told, before she sat down, to kindly fetch us the toaster from the kitchen, so we could plug it into the wall next to the couch and light our cigarettes on the armrest. As cultured, refined people do.

Why do we argue about such petty things? Perhaps it's because we've both had a long day at the office. Or perhaps, more likely, it's because we're both single and have nobody else to fight with anymore.

Diego might also be in a bad mood because of his break up.

'She wasn't Portuguese enough for my mother. Nothing tragic, I broke it off last week. And now she's moved onto another one of my friends.' So, the usual Johannesburg twenty-something story then. I suppose I'm his pseudo girlfriend anyway. And he's my surrogate boyfriend. It's as if we've been married sixty years and all the lust and wanton sex has disappeared, and now we're together for pure companionship, comfort and someone to banter with. Last night, we even fought about directions to the Jolly Roger coming from the Jo'burg CBD. Direction arguments are a common criterion of all romantic relationships.

PEAS: 'For God's sake, just phone Giulia for directions! She knows this part of town!'

DIEGO: 'No, it's somewhere down here.'

PEAS: 'No, it's not. We've been down this road already.'

Diego gives his opinion when asked for it, tells me when I'm being pathetic over a man, and manages to be caring and nice when asked. And when I don't want to see him, I go to bed. He complains that I'm too open with him ('I have period pains'/'my bunion is sore'/'please hold my hair back while I vomit') but deep down, I know he loves it.

Lizzy told me that Randy has a new girlfriend. Yes, it hurt. I battered her with a bunch of questions about whether his new squeeze is prettier than me, bigger busted, blonde or brunette, but eventually she got bored and refused to participate. The funny thing is that my response was automatic, I didn't actually care as much as I thought I would.

HAZY GROUND

I've put it off thinking about it for long enough, but there's no avoiding it anymore. Connor phoned me today and offered to buy me a ticket to India to see him. As much as I could use a break from Jo'burg and would absolutely love to see him, I'll have to give it some thought. I need to work out whether this feeling I have for him is just because I am missing him, or whether there is something more going on here.

CONNOR: 'I'll even sponsor your ticket. Now that I'm not forking out for Gwen anymore, I have some spare rupees.'

PEAS: 'You may just have to. My disposable income tends to go towards anything that comes in a frosted glass these days.'

CONNOR: 'I'd love to show you Mumbai; it'll blow your mind. I've even asked Lizzy to try and twist your arm.'

He sounded lonely. I wonder what he's eating, and whether he's had the notorious Delhi Belly yet. And if he's ever coming back! The thought that he might not fills me with dread.

RUBBER DUCK, PLEASE

I'm officially a loser. I might have officially been a loser my whole life, but now it's for certain. Why? My favourite part of the day is bath time. It's even usurped my previous favourite pastime of having noisy sex with a boyfriend on different pieces of furniture. Lizzy is the only other person who I know loves taking baths as much as I do.

LIZZY: 'Sidney, that foul boyfriend I once had when I was young and stupid, told me I was psycho because I lay in a bath for three hours once.'

PEAS: 'Surely he should've been happy that you bathed?'

LIZZY: 'He wasn't particularly hygienic himself, come to think of it. But dump me because I sit in the tub?'

PEAS: 'I've had some weird boyfriends, but that's sensational.'

LIZZY: 'Then there was Gary. Who couldn't stop washing his hands for two and a half seconds.'

PEAS: 'And he used to throw up a little when you touched his jersey, and he held his jersey over his hands when he opened doors ...'

LIZZY: 'Now he's dating Princess Eugenie, Fergie's daughter.'

PEAS: 'Shut up.'

LIZZY: 'Swear on my farm.'

PEAS: 'You're sure? Gary Perkins? Dating Princess Eugenie? Get off.'

LIZZY: 'Yeah, how great do I feel right now? I mean, farm, palace, farm, palace – what's he gonna choose?'

PEAS: 'Well I'd choose you. British Royalty is so ... germy. He probably still washes his hands ten times a day.'

LIZZY: 'You'd choose me?'

PEAS: 'Of course. You're totally lovable and adorable.'

LIZZY: 'I just can't wait until you and Connor realise you're in love and I become the ... very bathed bridesmaid.'

PEAS: 'What?'

LIZZY: 'It's only a matter of time.'

PEAS: 'Shut your pie-hole. He lives in India and he's hung-up over Gwendolyn. That's a completely unreasonable idea, Liz. I don't know how you could even suggest such a thing. Besides, since when have you ever been keen to wear bridesmaid apparel?'

LIZZY: 'We shall wait and see. Now go home and bath.'

PEAS: 'I still haven't decided whether to go on holiday with my dad yet.'

LIZZY: 'I think you should. Things need to be resolved face to face. '

PEAS: 'Thanks for pushing me. You know, to sort this out.'

LIZZY: 'You gotta be cruel to be kind sometimes. Now go bath.'

I start looking forward to my daily scrub at around 3:00 p.m. Pondering over and dreaming about which bubble bath to use (Radox or bath oil? Or bath salts? The options are endless) and whether to put a facemask on. This daydreaming is all while writing about, say, meatballs.

As I arrive home, I throw my keys down, and run myself a most sensationally hedonistic and loved-up bath fit for a princess. Even if the bathroom is plastered in babycrap-green tiles with a wilting shower curtain.

During my bath I sing to myself while blaring the likes of Andrea Boccelli over my speakers (like yesterday). If my cell phone – nonchalantly placed besides the soap – rings, I answer it and hope I don't drop it in. My bathing routine is regimented: the shave, the exfoliation, the washing and the stepping out. This is followed by a healthy lathering of creams, a pluck here and there and finally, a wrinkle check. Then, I slip on my underwear and my pyjamas, and pour myself a glass of, say, Porcupine Ridge wine. The entire ritual takes about two hours. And I enjoy every second of it, to the point where I'm starting to imagine doing the whole thing top to bottom twice a day.

I'm a bath addict; I'm a loser.

Is this what I've been reduced to without a boyfriend? Well I suppose Mum should be pleased I'm not a tik addict and rushing home to look for spare light bulbs in a flurry of excitement instead.

Connor and I talk to each other on Skype every other day or so. However, because I'm at the office, I have to make sure it's between 1:00 p.m. and 2:00 p.m. when The Sub is out to lunch. (Literally. Often she comes back tanked on wine spritzers.) It's always hard to have a proper conversation with him because the Evil One listens in with her satellite ears. He hasn't mentioned Gwendolyn in a while. I told him that I'd think about taking up his offer of going to see him. Possibly as soon as I'm brave enough to leave my comforting routine – like bath-time and *Home and Away*. These rituals are what I believe to be keeping me sane right now.

THE THING ABOUT GIULIA'S SCAB

After Lizzy's little outburst about Connor and I the other night, I decided it would be best to spend an evening with Giulia. I wanted to test to see if she would say anything about me and Connor of her own volition. If she did it would mean that both of my best friends were telling me that Connor and I should be having each other's babies. If the people closest to me think this, then the rumour needs to immediately be quashed and I need to start getting on with my life without thinking about Connor in a vaguely sexual manner. Giulia, however, didn't mention him. Instead her super scab got all the attention.

The woman went for a run two weeks ago and fell on the road in front of Hyde Park High. Now there's a big fat scab covering her kneecap. It's driving me crazy:

PEAS (whilst watching Grey's Anatomy): 'Would you please refrain from picking your scab?'

GIULIA: 'I can't help it. It's itchy as all hell.'

PEAS: 'You're dropping pieces of scab on the carpet.'

GIULIA: 'Don't worry, the maid's coming next week. Plus, it's not like you to be concerned about things like scabs on the floor.' (Peeling off a large piece of scab and flicking it into the ashtray.) 'There, are you happy?'

She gleefully carries on picking ... and flicking.

PEAS: 'Dude, I'm gonna light your scab.'

GIULIA: 'With what? The toaster?'

PEAS: 'Bring your knee to the armrest. Now.'

GIULIA: 'Hell, no.'

PEAS: 'Crap. The maid fucking took it back to the kitchen! Wait. I have a lighter. I'm going to ignite your scab. Show me your knee!'

GIULIA: 'No, you crazy bastard. You're not lighting anything that's attached to my body.'

PEAS: 'You're no fun.'

Having a flatmate has been wonderful and has probably saved my life on many occasions, but Giulia has taken the boundaries of friendship a step too far this time. Scratch scratch scratch. What could that be? Pants chaffing? Someone grating cheese? No, no, it's Giulia picking at her scab. Again. Almost compulsively. (Actually, there's no almost about it.) I do admit though that I will miss her when she moves out once her and Hendrik find a suitable place.

HUSBANKS

I'm still avoiding making a decision about the father and the Connor holiday issue. As a result, the couch and I are best mates, and the TV remote nestles like a glove between my palm and thumb. At the moment, I'm addicted to *My Name Is Earl*. I watch what I like when

I like, in a tracksuit.

Suddenly the idea of a husband is completely foreign to me. A boyfriend is foreign to me, so the idea that we're at that stage of our lives where people are starting to get married freaks me out. Panic! I'm so far behind! (Calm down, calm down ... you're happy, Peas ... breathe ...)

Lizzy and I have often laughed about husbands who get rich, find a trophy wife and drive expensive machines: Husbanks. In Jo'burg, the Husbank is not a rare species. Half the people we know are gunning for a Husbank. We concluded, after much debate, that we'll never need one though. It would be nice if Lizzy could find a husband who likes farming. Her sort-of kind-of new boyfriend does; they even chat about Massey Ferguson tractors and stuff. But Lizzy doesn't want a husband anyway. She loves the chase, but once it's hers, she runs away from commitment faster than you can say boyfriend. The few boyfriends she's had have cried buckets over Lizzy, because she eventually left them. (Barring Gary Perkins, of course.)

Peas: 'Right, so you've helped me to see some things about myself? It's *your* turn.'

Lizzy: 'And what exactly is wrong with the way I'm living my life?'

Peas: 'Well for one, while I try and grab hold of someone and squeeze onto them for dear life, you do quite the opposite. You run. It has to be said. And what's with not even admitting that you have a boyfriend? '

Lizzy: 'I know, so what?'

Peas: 'Well don't you think you might be missing out on something great simply because you're terrified of being tied down?'

Lizzy: 'Yes, I do. But I'd rather not risk it. I'm happy, so why should I change? *You* weren't happy, you had to change. I am happy – don't fix something that ain't broke; ever heard of that?'

Peas: 'And this new sort-of boyfriend? Will you run when he asks about a future with you?'

LIZZY: 'Probably. But that's because I am *selective*, Peas, and I know he's not The One. I can have fun without getting completely attached.'

PEAS: 'Well, if only I was as robotic and as unfeeling as you! Jesus, Lizzy, you can't live your life as an automated machine!'

LIZZY: 'It's worked fine thus far.'

PEAS: 'I don't believe you. You numb your emotions as much as I did, with alcohol and excessive clubbing. Perhaps you need to look within too.'

LIZZY: 'I know I do, Peas. I know. I will face up when I meet some-one great, like, say, Connor, and then I'll readjust.'

PEAS: 'Okay, Robot Lady.'

My so-called laissez-faire single lifestyle is fun, but at times it does seem to wear thin. It's hard to keep blissfully self-absorbed and ex-cessively glad you're not spooning someone when:

- Giulia has a boyfriend.
- Bennet has a girlfriend.
- Lizzy has a sort-of boyfriend, but won't tell me his name. The moment she tells me, she'll panic and run for the hills.
- Helen has a boyfriend.
- Christine has a boyfriend, who is Bennet.
- Anthony has a girlfriend – I think.
- Dierdra dumped hers yesterday, but the day before that she had a boyfriend.

We single people are an endangered species in the City of Hook-Ups And Have A Lot Of Sex. I'm gradually becoming an outsider because everyone has someone. On a bad day, I just want to revert back to my old ways and grab onto the nearest male I can find. I am de-termined to stay strong, though. I've worked hard at being a happy recluse over the last couple months. I'm okay being mad, single Aunty Peas at future family events, and the thought almost makes me smile. (The actual chomper-showing grin is a work in progress.)

'Oh look. Mad Aunty Peas is at the whiskey again. And she bought all thirty-two of her cats with her to the wedding ...'

Whatever happens, it won't be cats. Watch all the bambinos recoil in terror when I rock up with thirty-two iguanas. And I'll probably wear blue eye-shadow too.

Also. Sex. Don't think I'm not constantly reminded of how much sex some of these people are having.

DAD

My father called me again. I think he's trying to over-compensate.

'Are you thinking about the holiday?'

'I will, Dad.'

'Oh, and Peas? Have I been a terrible father?'

I pondered for a moment. 'No, Dad. You've just been a different father. There're some things you've done for me no other father could've.'

Suddenly everything is starting to change around me. I may have a long way to go, but I think I'm starting to see through the fog. Randy might've seemed perfect but if he was so perfect for me, then he would've stuck around. The hate is starting to abate; I now know what I want and what I don't. And being in a loveless relationship isn't part of the picture.

I don't need to be the life of the party *every weekend*. Parties will always be there. If I'm single forever, then best I start looking out for number one. And that means facing my issues head on and not always putting on the brave (often drunken) face. And quite frankly, I'm not ashamed to admit that I bloody well enjoy watching television at home, without having to talk to anyone.

In the midst of my self-observation, Helen called.

HELEN: (Whispering.) 'Peas, it's me. Help.'

(Muffled echoing sounds, like she's standing in a broom closet or toilet cubicle.)

PEAS: 'Dude, where are you talking?'

HELEN: 'In the bathroom. Oh my fuck, you're not going to believe this. I am at that dinner party with Dude I'm Kind Of Seeing, right? And guess who is here?'

PEAS: 'Who?'

HELEN: 'I've been placed between Guy I Kissed This Weekend and Girl Who Just Kissed Another Guy I Also Kissed This Weekend. And she knows.'

PEAS: 'What? Just what kind of nightmare dinner party are you at?'

HELEN: 'Nightmare. Dude this is so hectic, and I'm so drunk and obnoxious right now, oh God help.'

PEAS: 'Calm down. What Girl Who Kissed What Guy?'

HELEN: 'You know the guy I kissed this weekend? Not my, um, boyfriend, the other guy? Well he snogged this girl too, and she's fucking here. And I'm sitting in between them.'

PEAS: 'This is priceless.'

HELEN: 'Fuck. I have to go back and eat dessert.'

PEAS: 'Classic. Good luck with that, dude. Don't think I'd cope.'

HELEN: 'Shit, I gotta go. I hope they didn't hear this conversation.'

PEAS: 'It would be funny if they did though.'

HELEN: 'Bye.'

And then there's having fun. I must remember to do that. Not everything has to be all serious and intense. But, I am glad it was Helen stuck in the bathroom for once, not me. If I just move over and make room, there's more than enough space for everyone's dramas.

Yet another call from Dad yesterday. He's really trying hard, I have to give him that. At least he's stopped talking to me on a phone while flying across the razor-sharp mountains of the Drakensberg, at any rate. He's now come up with a plausible holiday plan, knuckling down and being serious, perhaps for the first time I can remember.

DAD: 'Peas, besides the fact we obviously need to talk about stuff' (he said this in a grave tone) 'flying around by myself also gets quite lonely you know.'

PEAS: 'I thought you had a squeeze you were flying with all over the country.'

DAD: 'No, Denise wanted to tie me down. So our last stop was Calvinia. It was a silent trip home, a very silent trip, might I add.'

PEAS: 'What about Cheryl?'

DAD: 'Cheryl? *Cheryl?* No, no. No. Cheryl was ... eccentric.'

PEAS: 'I'm trying to work out why that wouldn't be an especially perfect match.'

DAD: 'Nah. Eccentric means you're weird. I'm not weird.'

PEAS: 'Dad.'

DAD: 'Okay, so I'm a bit ADD. But that's why I need your help!'

PEAS: 'Of course you're not. Even if everyone says you're ADD, Dad, don't listen to them.' (My attempt at humour.)

DAD: 'You're not seeing anyone at the moment are you? What happened to Rodney?'

PEAS: 'Randy, Dad. Oh what the hell ... Rodney and I were over months ago. I'm not attached. Maybe next time you can listen when I call you in tears telling you that a boy just dumped me.'

DAD: 'Are you ready for our father-daughter sabbatical? We can call it our sabbatical.'

PEAS: 'I said I'm thinking about it, but I also have commitments.'

DAD: 'What commitments?'

PEAS: 'Unlike you, Dad, I have a job, and other social commitments.'

DAD: 'Social commitments? Like what?'

PEAS: 'You know, boozing and getting messy.'

DAD: 'Enough. We need to sort this out once and for all.'

PEAS: 'Should I resign today or next week, Dad, i.e. before my deadline?'

DAD: 'Do it. Just think, me and you flying over the Bazaruto Archipelago in Mozambique. I've always wanted to see Margaruque.'

PEAS: 'Okay, that sounds better.'

DAD: 'Pack your bags.'

He's pretty adamant. Now I have to face up to what I've started, I can't back out now and am ninety-nine per cent sure that I'll apply for leave to go on holiday. If I was to go visit Connor in India, I'd have to wait until spring is over however. Connor says it's monsoon season which makes walking outside very unpleasant. I'm actually very excited about life at the moment.

Perhaps there'll always be a piece of me that's completely fucked up. Maybe someone will even love that about me one day. Yes, I come with a brand new set of hang-ups and cynicisms because of my experiences, but I reckon it makes me less shallow, more in touch with myself and wiser.

If only Connor was here to witness the new me.

Chapter Twelve

ERA END

Now that I'm certain of what I want and need from a relationship, it seems the perfect time for Anthony and I to finalise our 'divorce'. For the love of God, it's taken almost a year for Anthony to collect the rest of his things from our old flat. Since he moved back home, he hasn't needed many of the appliances so I have continued using them. Last night he came to pick them up.

ANTHONY: 'You can have the side tables. I never really liked them anyway.'

PEAS: 'You bought them. Don't you remember the argument we had at Furniture City? I thought they were the ugliest pieces of furniture ever to have graced this earth.'

ANTHONY: 'No ways. I'd never have wanted to buy them. They're yours.'

PEAS: 'No. They're *yours*.'

ANTHONY: 'Well, let's leave them on the pavement and see what happens to them.'

PEAS: 'They'll be there for three months until the rubbish bin guys are forced to remove them. Say, do you want the Anthony Shapiro mugs? It's cool.'

ANTHONY: 'Nah, but I'd like the New York Smoothie Maker if that's cool.'

PEAS: 'Sure.'

Anthony will always be very special to me since we shared so much together. He was, after all, my first love. Now, he's finally moving out of his folks' place and into a new flat down the road with a mate. I didn't ask but I have a sneaky suspicion that he may even be seeing someone. And if I'm right, it doesn't upset me all that much. He deserves to be happy.

In the pouring rain, Giulia and I helped load his stuff into the car. I felt completely flat afterwards. Flat and immovable, I slumped on the couch dejectedly. I even drank a beer. I don't drink beer unless I'm in Belgium or Germany.

I suppose that this is life. It seems that in my trivial little existence, things do change. It all has to end up somewhere, right? Surely everything that happens, no matter how seemingly insignificant, has to somehow contribute to a bigger (and perhaps better) picture?

FUDGING DIET

One drawback of being happy is that I am getting fat. I've started consuming copious amounts of food. When I'm sad, I don't eat; when I'm happy I eat all the pies.

Yesterday evening, after consuming a bastardised version of my grandmother's *rougaille*, and chatting to Diego about Chinese impoverishment, I realised that my love handles are muffin-topping over my jeans. Time to start looking after my body as well as my mental health since spring is upon us.

So, I'm doing the following:
- Using toner day and night, even if I don't have make-up on.
- Drinking alcohol only once a week and in moderation.
- Going on a swearing diet.

The last item is going to take the most discipline. It has to be done however, since Helen complained that her new company blocks my e-mails.

Access to peasontoast@gmail.com has been denied and
blocked by WebMarshal™
Text download (TEXT, 82180 bytes) was restricted by the text
censor rule 'Block Offensive Language'.
TextCensor Script 'Offensive Language' triggered with total
weighting of 16:
Expression 'bitch' triggered 4 times, weighting 8
Expression 'crap' triggered 1 times, weighting 2
Expression 'fuck' triggered 3 times, weighting 6
Contact your WebMarshal administrator if you need access to
this site for business purposes.
WebMarshal Server: SNAP (Version: 3.5.2.16)

I swear like a sailor; if I read through my diaries, I'd most probably balk at the atrocities that have spewed forth from my fingertips. In order to act like a proper lady in the company of others, best I try and curb this nasty little habit now. Nip it in the bud before I'm just an unpleasant, grouchy old woman with a mouth like a sewer.

The problem is, well, I just love the word fuck. It's just so expressive. However, I'm going to have to trade it in for these words instead:

- Effing: The effing taxi cut in front of me. Twice. For eff's sake.
- Fudge: Fudge you, fudgewit. I missed my fudging deadline.
- Fack: A less-caustic derivative of fuck. But too close to actual word, so not allowed.

Instead of shit, these are the alternatives:

- Sherbet: Sherbet Herbert, if you do that one more time, I'm going to lose my rag.
- Sheesh: That's an incredible tree, sheesh.
- Shait/shite: Not allowed. See 'fack'.

Other foul words I cannot use (think of this list as me helping myself to the family buffet one last time, before a week's worth of celery and carrots):

Fuck, shit, the shits, shitters, wank, wanky, pisswilly, fuckwanker.

Eff it, I'm probably going to go back to being a notorious potty-mouth, but it's worth a shot. I wrote to Connor and told him I wasn't going to swear anymore. He said it was a pity, since he finds my dirty mouth rather attractive.

NOT EVERYTHING IS AS IT SEEMS

Relationship comparison used to really get up my nose. Especially since my relationships haven't been all roses and champagne. I'd see the happy-looking coupling from a distance and think, 'But why doesn't *my* boyfriend do that?' But it's actually a bad habit. I noticed a couple on the street yesterday and for a moment felt so relieved not to have to deal with any of this right now.

GIRL: 'Well, fuck you. I saw you dancing with her, what do you take me for? *Stupid*?'

BOY: 'Well, yes, because you are stupid.'

GIRL: 'You need to emigrate.'

BOY: 'I am planning on it. Like tomorrow. Watch me, lady, watch me walk to Flight Centre right now!'

GIRL: 'I'm watching. Start walking, asshole! As long as you there and I'm here, that's just. Fine. With. Me.'

BOY: 'Good.'

GIRL: 'You're a fucker.'

BOY: 'So are you.'

GIRL: 'That's not possible, because you're the biggest fucker in the whole world.'

BOY: 'See? I'm walking,' (walking backwards into a pot plant) 'I'm walking!'

(I was embarrassed at having to walk straight through this altercation, 'Terribly sorry, excuse me.')

This incident reminded me of four things:
1) Hells bells, relationships are hard work.
2) Nevertheless, never argue in an open street.
3) I bet he not only danced with her, he shagged her too.
4) Relationship comparison is the enemy in any circumstance.

Helen has set me up with someone. Of all the nerve. Doesn't she realise that a blind date is the last thing I want (or need)? I also know she tried him out and decided that he's actually better suited to me. I just love getting sloppy seconds. But, I'll go simply because I have no plans for Saturday. Admittedly, I do miss going to restaurants with someone. The wine, the food, the hot flush of the bar rash after one too many gin and tonics, the gentle nuzzling beneath the table, getting to know them better, the going-home-together-and-taking-off-of-clothes-in-a-frenzy scenario ...

Maybe he'll even wear a crisp white shirt.

THANKS HELEN
... for nothing. No wonder she didn't want to date this guy. What a disaster. I don't even want to talk about it. I'm certain he snorted a line of coke before our date.

Also worth a mention: how much garlic does the guy eat? I eat a fair amount, my French family has trained me since I was a mere child, but this was just ridiculous.

> MUM: 'Peas, where are you? Why don't you phone your old mother anymore? I mean, I was only in labour for you for *eighteen* hours. You got stuck in my birth canal and I had to be rushed to surgery.'

Peas: 'Thanks, Mum, for letting me be born. Having me was the ultimate bitch, I know. I have nothing to report, hence my silence. A bad date, late nights and singledom. I'll call you when something exciting happens, promise.'

I'm angry with Connor. He seems to have forgotten about me, I Skyped him at work and demanded to know why he hadn't been in touch. He replied that it's because he's battling with something important at the moment.

PEAS: 'What?'

CONNOR: 'Just relationship issues.'

PEAS: 'Don't tell me it's Gwendolyn again?'

CONNOR: 'Yes. And other stuff.'

PEAS: 'Care to talk about it?'

CONNOR: 'I can't.'

PEAS: 'Fine then ... Why can't you confide in me anymore?'

CONNOR: 'Because I don't know how to right now.'

PEAS: 'You've always been able to tell me anything! What's your problem, Connor?'

CONNOR: 'It's not about Gwendolyn. She's only getting up my nose because I don't know how to get rid of her. She keeps on calling and asking for another chance.'

PEAS: 'Oh for God's sake. Why don't you just move on already? If you're that unhappy, you need to sort yourself out. Or come home.'

CONNOR: 'I know this already. I just can't talk about what's going on in my head.'

PEAS: 'So now you can't tell me stuff anymore? Fine. I'm really hurt. Chat to you later.'

CONNOR: 'It's not what you think. You've got the wrong end of the stick. It's that Peas ... gosh this is so hard ... I think ...'

PEAS (interrupting): 'I don't do "cryptic", Connor; talk to me straight up or don't talk at all. Goodbye.'

Now I feel really guilty. I completely overreacted. If the poor guy is having a tough time and can't confide just yet, why did I shoot him down? I need to talk to him face to face. It's so hard with him being across the globe. There's something else going on here between us that I can't quite put my finger on.

I had much work to get through at the office, which was delayed by The Sub procrastinating while she should have been subbing my every article. So we missed our deadline. Ridiculously pissed off and extremely disappointed with the human species, I almost blew a gasket and stomped out of the office.

SUB: 'Your "Goulash In The Midlands" article, where is it?'

PEAS: 'I handed it to you *last week*, you'll find it's been *on your desk* for a week now.'

SUB: 'Oh. Well you should've told me it was on my desk.'

PEAS: 'I did. Five times.'

SUB: 'Well, clearly I was busy with other much more important stuff, because it's not here anymore.'

PEAS: 'Oh you mean while I wrote one of your articles for you? The "Provolone Cheese: Is It Even Cheese?" piece?'

She's such a nightmare.

Poor Lizzy was smashed in the face with a hockey ball and concussed over the weekend. But I was also hit by something. Could've been Connor, in fact it most certainly was Connor. It resembled a forty-ton bus, but since I was hit by it, I cannot be sure the precise measurements of said bus. The bus, in passing, left me on the road to die a slow and painful death. The sign written on it said: PEAS. IS. SUCH. A. LOSER.

I reckon the bus left the Peas Is A World-Class Loser station at roughly 12:09 p.m., to stop at I'm So Sick Of Feeling Fucked Up at precisely 1:03 p.m., to stop at When Will Life Be Cool Again terminal at 1:05 p.m., halting briefly at Royally Hacked Off With Earth at 1:08 p.m., then a momentous halt at Could I Be In Love With Connor (did I just say that?) thereafter, and almost immediately afterwards, a sail through No, I Must Be On Drugs, and, upon hitting me in the chest, left me with a 'Monday Blues' sign yesterday.

Luckily, today, I am stable enough to dodge the bus with the sign saying 'Peas, Life Isn't Going To Get Better', which, on impact, would kill me dead and proper. I still feel bad about how my conversation ended with Connor. Should I confess to him about these un-friend thoughts I'm having about him? Perhaps if I tell him whatever he has to tell me must be easier.

Over and above that, a pressing matter involving skew posters in our flat prevails. We think Pretty our maid has been smoking Sweet Mary Jane on the job. Our Sweet Mary, that is.

Pretty cleaned the place yesterday, and while Lizzy with a swollen face, Diego, Giulia and I shared a pizza, we noticed was that my giant Marilyn Monroe poster hanging in the hallway was hanging at a bizarre angle. Marilyn falls off the wall – all six seismic feet of her, almost all the time. So Giulia bought Prestik and asked Pretty to please hang up the flagging posters dotted around our crib properly. But she'd hung every poster at a thirty-degree angle to the ceiling. And not positioned in the middle of the wall (where it had been before) either, but rather jammed into the corner and off-centre. You have to cock your head to the side to look at them.

We figured that either the lady has a frightening lack of spatial semblance, or more likely, judging by the half-horizontal way they'd been Prestricked, she was taking the mickey. She has to be: the things are so squiff, it can only be deliberate. But there is another alternative. We sometimes leave stray marijuana dregs around the apartment. I know if I were her, I'd smoke 'em. On the other hand, perhaps it's just the Windolene fumes. Inhaling them would definitely make scrubbing the toilet less menial. And changing the toilet roll would give her a good giggle, I'm certain. Pretty probably has a right frigging gas, toking it up, or getting high on Mr Muscle, and cleaning our place until it sparkles. I'd love to see her in action, I mean if she enjoys it, by all means let her do it. But next time we'll hang the posters.

Although, that said, we haven't necessarily moved the posters and repositioned them upright. We call it charm.

Connor called late last night. To apologise. I was relieved. I too apologised for being so irrational and was just about to confess that I was feeling strange about the dynamics between us, when he said he needed to give it one more try with Gwendolyn because they'd been through so much, he at least owed her that much. I suppose they have gone halfway across the globe to be exact. So, even thought it was difficult, I told him to do what his instinct was telling him.

What's this dull thudding in my chest? I'm so sick of the G-Factor. The Gwendolyn he doesn't even love, but tries hard to. I'm disappointed at this latest turn of events. I still wasn't clear about my own feelings and wanted time to try and sort them out, perhaps with Connor. Now, it's all been decided.

Anyway, am I crazy? He's in India. I am here, still suffering with spurts of depression, but gradually getting better and stronger each day. It's a wild notion to even consider, this 'thing' with my best mate – my best mate! Thank God he wants Gwendolyn again. It would just ruin the friendship.

WHO ATE ALL THE PIES?

Many women eat when they're grief stricken, depressed, sad or angry. Not me. When I'm any of those things I simply stop eating.

I'll open the fridge, look at the cheese for about five minutes, maybe pick up a piece of leftover chicken, put it back, then close the fridge. This ritual takes place almost compulsively when I'm at home alone feeling desperately sorry for myself. You can't make me eat when I'm down.

Until a month or two ago, I involuntarily could not finish a meal. I really wanted to, but settled instead on a most unsavoury diet consisting of cigarettes, coffee and biltong. And occasionally, for fear of contracting scurvy, the odd orange.

I forced protein down my throat. This is the most important food group in maintaining any muscle tissue, so over the last four months I have been gnawing unattractively on biltong snapsticks of bulk-sized proportions. But that's about it.

Then something strange happened. I got happy.

I sort of slid into a bubble of self-absorbed content. I just let go. But that's not the only thing that's let go.

Now that I am officially happy and sane, I have started stuffing my face again, and am afraid I'm going to look like the Michelin Man if I carry on this way.

Fat and happy is not going to get me laid.

Let's take stock of what has been consumed over the last three days:

2 x tubs of Gino Ginelli Choc Nut Italiano. Straight out the tub. For dinner.

3 x packets of biltong snapsticks. For breakfast.

1 x Caesar salad

4 x Woolies sandwiches

1 x lasagne

3 x risotto con funghi

4 x slabs of Top Deck

5 x spaghetti a la surprises

1 x wet, fatty biltong slices. For lunch.

1 x box hazelnut Nutties

1 x Westcliff breakfast (eggs, salmon, mushroom conglomerate)

1 x apple

1 x fruit salad

Right. What am I compensating for, one wonders? Happiness? No, got that. Starvation? No, not emaciated. Carbo-loading for a race? Um, no. Sex? Ka-ching. That's what's missing.

BABS, YOU'RE AN IDIOT

I was in one of those moods where I was keen to stick Barbra Streisand on full blast (FIRST MISTAKE), take a bath and wield a glass of La Motte after an epic day in heels. Following a long day spent at the Sandton Convention Centre in and out of food presentations and writing like a bitch onto my notepad, I was tired. Hence, the mood, amplified by Babs' quite frankly, unbelievably stupid lyrics. She sings this ultra-corny duet with the formidable Celine Dion who, I believe, is asking her for love advice. To which she responds:

Tell him (Oh yes)
Tell him that the sun and moon rise in his eyes
Reach out to him
Tender words so soft and sweet
... I've been there with my heart out in my hands
But what you must understand
You can't let the chance to love him pass you by
Love will be the gift you give yourself
Your love can't be denied
The truth will set you free ...

Soon, I'd heard enough. These bitches were ruining my bath. After jumping out of the tub, leaving a trail of Radox bubbles from the bathroom to the hi-fi in the lounge, I switched the bloody thing off. Babs isn't the brightest billboard on the highway. This annoys me, since I'll bet her ballads have influenced thousands of romantic liaisons. I do think she has a voice like crushed satin, but still. She must be thick. A sixty-something woman, who has surely been through heartache before must be taking the piss to be serenading Celine with such misguided advice. Or she's trying to fuck with Celine's head by basically telling her to profess her undying love to a man.

This is the biggest load of pants I've ever heard. Now I may only be (cough) almost twenty-six years old, but I at least know better. And if I were to dish out any advice, it would be:

Never, ever, ever mention the 'L' word to a man as long as you live, if at all possible. I did this once and the man ran out of my door and never looked back. (Although I'm started to think I shagged him out of the door, but I think the 'L' word was more to blame.) Actually, just don't fall in love. Never define your lust, longing and sexual attraction towards someone as love. Trust me.

The exception of course, is if a man tells you he loves you first. If you do fall in love with someone, 1) you're a hopeless case and 2) keep it to yourself. Barbra Streisand is a nutcase. She's way out of control. Someone put a leash on that woman. 'The sun and moon rise in your eyes.' Peeeyuke. And to think that Barry Gibb and company did tours with this chick. There are impressionable teenagers out there for goodness' sake! Those who'll take these lyrics seriously, tell their men they love them and then cry for months afterwards wondering what the hell they did wrong when he never calls back. Have some social responsibility, Barbra Streisand, I mean really.

Anyway, I know better and that's the main thing.

Another detrimental factor concerning Barbra Streisand is that she made me think obsessively about Connor last night. I have to snap out of this. He's with Gwendolyn, and he doesn't feel anything for me but pure, unadulterated friendship.

STOP THE CLOCKS

September has arrived: my birthday month. I always look forward to my birthday, but not this year. Usually I have a whopper of a party, and have a dickens of a time celebrating being a year older and toasting my minimal achievements between now and my last birthday.

But I'm not much in the mood for celebration. In fact, I just want to forget the whole affair altogether. I'm completely dreading it. Actually, I'm a trifle depressed because I'm not sure who'd remember it besides my parents; and I'm turning twenty-six, meaning I'm closer to thirty than twenty-one. I've also, most importantly, always had someone to make it special for me for the last five years. And now I won't have breakfast brought to me in bed or a good birthday roll in the hay from a man who loves me.

As a Virgo, I'm over-analytical, precise and obsessed with perfection. Add to that my perpetual angst. Virgos were clearly born at the worst part of the year. For the last three months, my stupid horoscope has been nothing short of disastrous. We've basically had a run of bad luck since May. And birthday month or not, it's not getting any better.

Instead of 'you will feel happier on the 4th', 'money will come your way', 'you look ravishing,' Virgos are getting: 'July is filled with challenges for you. Hibernation might be a good option.' Maybe August will be better? Oh no, the fucking planetary constellations aren't quite done dishing out disappointment to the poor, unassuming Virgo: 'August, you'll be inundated with work, but not necessarily be paid for it.' September? 'You're being victimised. As a result you become a wallflower and feel crappy about your physical appearance.'

Meanwhile, Libra seems to have all fun and games. As does Taurus. 'You have a packed social diary, your admirers are endless and the dough is rolling in. Your sexual charisma is almost tangible.'

Christ, are you kidding me? My swearing diet is now off. Fuck the world. I am buying a hamster.

From: peasontoast@gmail.com
To: giuliabriattore@itye.com
Subject: cute, fluffy and warm

I've given up pretending I need nothing. It's a number of things; maybe I'm just a little over-sensitive this week, but I can't deny my state of spinsterhood much longer. Can we get a cat, doll face? I'm settling in for the single long haul and perhaps it'll be easier if I have a furry creature with which to share it. It's not because I WANT a boyfriend. I really, really don't. I just want something I can squeeze every now and then. Do you hate cats?

From: giuliabriattore@itye.com
To: peasontoast@gmail.com
Re: cute, fluffy and warm

No. Absolutely not! I am allergic and, yes, I hate cats. You hate cats too. So no. If you get one, it's a downhill slope. You'll never get laid again. Buy a hamster, I'm okay with that. Besides, you know I'll be gone as soon as Hendrik finds us a place close enough to his tight-knit Calvinist parents and close enough to my Catholic folks. I know a place where you buy those supersonic cages with all those tunnel thingies attached. P.S. Don't pretend, missy. It's Connor. I know it, you know it, but I shan't say anything more.

From: connor@irishcarbomb.com
To: peasontoast@gmail.com
Subject: monsoon trouble

Okay, this is hectic. But Gwendolyn and I have broken up, for good it would seem. It's final this time, even though I know I said that after Gwendolyn's Sharm El Sheik hook-up, I really mean it. This time I really do. Our entire relationship has been somewhat ridiculous – I'm the first to admit. Now, she's started dating my landlord, who happens to live two doors down from me. Sometimes I hear them arguing and then I turn up the volume on my iPod.

Now I know I'm putting this out there, but I think you've had six months of getting over Dennis – or was it Gareth? Whatever, I want you to consider coming over to visit. I'll take some time off, we can go to Goa. There are things I've been thinking about, mulling over, with regards to you, you and me, and I think a holiday together might be a good idea. Besides, an exotic experience would do you the world of good.

Admittedly, this very second is the wrong time, there's may-hem everywhere. During monsoon season the tuk-tuks cause massive traffic jams and sometimes the gutters burst. Don't be alarmed, this place is like another planet, but it's also amazing. You'll love the colours, fabrics, food, and I happen to know of some crazy nightclubs that we can go squeak some takkie at. I won't drop my trousers unless you ask me to. Promise. Please come over. Please. I'll help you financially if you need.

Don't reply unless it's with an answer.

Love you.
Connor

What? *What?* Do I take this seriously? Or will he be back with Gwen tomorrow? I sat on it for a few hours before deciding to reply in a rational non-emotional way. I don't think I'm in a position to be strung along right now, I mean he sounds like he really wants me to go over, but would it be a good idea for *me* if he's still hung up over Gwendolyn and just needs company? Or is he perhaps also feeling this confusion about 'us'? I can't read between the lines, men don't do that stuff. My head hurts. My hands are trembling. This is ridiculous.

From: peasontoast@gmail.com
To: connor@irishcarbomb.com
Re: monsoon trouble

Congrats on the Goodbye Gwendolyn thing. Is it honestly for real now, or am I going to get an e-mail next week telling me about her moving back in after she's bored with the landlord?

I'm glad you invited me to come and visit you in India.

There's a lot going around in my head right now, Connor, and much of it has got to do with you. About how we've been communicating lately, or rather how we haven't really been communicating. I'll be in touch.

P.S. Sorry I haven't given you an answer yet, but I will. Soon.

Chapter Thirteen

Time heals all wounds until you mess with the hair. All I can think of now is Connor. How terribly *frustrating*. Aargh! I thought it best to maybe just focus on my hair follicles, with dire results.

In the wake of my potential Indian adventure, I tried to change my image without consulting Giulia first. She often gets irrationally upset if I go and buy something 'daringly kooky' that she'll later describe as 'gulag chic'. But I couldn't stop fiddling and pacing, so I had to do something.

Giulia: 'What did I tell you about not consulting me first? Are you loco?'

Peas: 'I need instant gratification, you know that!'

Giulia: 'And look where that got you. Frankly, I'm appalled.'

Peas: 'You know how they recommend you to do the "strand test" first? It's not completely pathetic, that little piece of fine print. Situated somewhere between "don the gloves", "set the timer" and "mix the peroxide in with the colour sachet".'

The box clearly indicated that the colour was Plum Dark Brown. You know, chocolatey brown with a hint of plum. I wanted to make my somewhat dull brown locks shiny, transform them into dark and tumbling tresses which, when the sun caught them, would be a glittering plummy fusion of beauty.

I followed the instructions. I left the dye on for twenty minutes. Then rinsed. Oh horror of all horrors. It was purple. I was the proud owner of a purple head of hair. Not mauve. Not lilac. Not blue.

Purple. Purple Opel Corsa purple. Freak show purple. Teenage Goth purple. Grape. Violent violet. I'll have to re-dye it tomorrow.

Then Giulia arrived, immediately thereafter followed by her family. Recently purpled and pyjama-clad, I greeted her Papa, Luigi, and Mama, Alessia, while Giulia screamed at them in Italian demanding – I can only guess – to know why they'd arrived unannounced. She was half naked when they arrived, having a piccolo canoodle with Hendrik at the time. I escaped from the Itye war of words and throwing of colanders by retreating to my boudoir in silence.

Suddenly there are all these travel plans to consider. Dad phoned to announce that we are going to Mozambique for our bonding-break in his tiny plane.

DAD: 'You're coming right?'

PEAS: 'Dad … I might be going to India to see Connor.'

DAD: 'Well, that's all right, I mean, you can go afterwards. You can fly to Johannesburg from Vilankulos. I always liked Colin, I'm glad you're going.'

PEAS: 'I'm going to take a lot of leave. Both of these breaks have to happen … somehow.'

I'm not sure if it's wise or if I'm jumping the gun with Connor; going to see him might make things worse. But, then at least I will know for sure, clear up these muddled feelings. The only friend I have confided in about Connor is Lizzy. Only because she guessed. Bennet doesn't have a clue what's going on and until I know what's really happening, I think I'll remain mum.

But I'm definitely going with Dad. I think there's much he needs to get off his chest. And if he's ready to open up, then I can't miss this opportunity.

Over the horizon lies a clearing.

I've received another e-mail from Connor. This one made my stomach do flick-flacks.

From: connor@irishcarbomb.com
To: peasontoast@gmail.com
Subject: Perhaps this is more direct

Peas, I can't keep this to myself any more, as much as I have
tried. You're a drama queen, you're insane, intense, funny,
intelligent and misunderstood. You're also stubborn and
self-righteous and a nightmare when you drink cane and your
singing voice sounds like a combine harvester scraping over
the tarmac. (Sorry, but someone had to say it.) But I love all
these things about you. You're my best friend and I actually,
I've never told you before but I also think you're sexy. And the
reason you need to come over here is because I want to know
whether what I'm feeling is real.

See, I've had some epiphanies lately. About life and stuff. India
does this to you. But I believe that deep down I have always
known you were more special to me than just a friend, and
maybe you're shocked and have never thought about me in the
same manner, and for that I'm sorry. It's just taken me some
growing up and deep contemplation to admit it. It took guts to
spill this revelation to you but, on some level, I think you might
feel the same way. Am I wrong?

Connor
Xx

Oh my God. Is this real? What a relief! I've read and re-read the
e-mail, shaking a little, smiling a lot. I'm dancing around my desk.
The Sub is shooting me looks of disdain, but I don't care.

The time is nigh for some much-needed advice.

PEAS: 'Lizzy, what do you make of that?'

LIZZY: 'I've always known, muchacha. Always known. Listen to
Wise Lizzy.'

PEAS: 'And why did you only say something last month?'

LIZZY: 'Because you had to hear it from him, not me. But I also think you're ready to hear it now. You like him don't you?'

PEAS: 'He lives in India. *He lives in India.*'

LIZZY: 'Love knows no boundaries.'

PEAS: 'That is so lame.'

LIZZY: 'I know. Puke. Next time I speak to you though, I suspect you'll have booked a ticket.'

PEAS: 'I can't just go. I have ... stuff to do here.'

LIZZY: 'Like articles on carrots julienne and ostrich steak? Give me a break.'

GIULIA: 'Book a ticket. If you don't, I'll clobber you over the head with my colander. You love him, he loves you ... stop complicating things. '

PEAS: 'Get off the turps. I haven't even decided yet.'

From: mrtoast@pimpinallovertheworld.com
To: peasontoast@gmail.com
Subject: Mozambique? Don't make me MOZAMBLEAK, Peas

Hello my darling

I know, I know – you have a life and commitments and I know you've thought about Mozambique, but I need a firm affirmative answer here! You have to help me. Cheryl found out about Denise last night and I'm in a little bit of pickle. I'm coming up to Jo'burg tomorrow, and whether you like it or not we're flying to Mozambique for the weekend.

Who knew women could get so highly strung about stuff like this? I mean, I didn't propose to any of them, and I'm certainly not getting my vasectomy reversed.

Much love,
Dad

From: peasontoast@gmail.com
To: mrtoast@pimpinallovertheworld.com
Re: Mozambique? Don't make me MOZAMBLEAK, Peas

Hi Dad

Okay, I'm coming. And I'm excited. But there are going to be conditions, Dad. I don't want what happened on the Camping Trip That Shall Not Be Mentioned of '98 to resurface again. This means:

No erratic behaviour, e.g. stopping the car on railway tracks until the train is five metres away to test the limits of the station wagon's pull-off thrust and nearly killing us all. *Car/ plane/other vehicles – all apply.

I will never, ever eat bully beef. Never have, never will. In fact, I do not want to hear the words 'bully beef'. And frying it is not normal.

I get to take a reasonable amount of luggage. In other words, a bag AND a toiletry bag – not one or the other. Making me choose is bordering on child abuse, Dad.

We only fly into legal places. Like if Swaziland says we can't fly over it, then we are NOT flying over Swaziland.

We need to talk. No ifs or buts, no avoiding the subject – I have a bone to pick with you. And you need to help me understand you more. Got it?

I'll take Friday off, but my leave is tight. You need to write my boss a letter saying I have a family obligation that day. That way I have an alibi in case The Sub interferes with his decision.

If you can comply by these firm requests, I'll come along. Promise.

We will talk about stuff. This is a bonding father-daughter trip.
And whether you like it or not, there's going to be no sweeping
under the carpet of issues. Are we clear? We're going to talk
like adults. Both of us.

Love,
Peas

COMING TO A HEAD ... LITERALLY

Yesterday was a bad day for so many reasons. Things have come
to a head, quite literally, at the office. I walked into the boardroom,
where the dear Sub appeared to be giving my big boss a wee bit of
special attention. Luckily he was already doing his zipper up and she
was getting off her knees as I burst in.

'Oh, so the rumours are true then,' I couldn't help murmuring
under my breath.

The Sub, of course, blushing, insisted that she was helping him
with his hem (stapling it up, 'because stitches are too permanent').
He then showed me the staples on his hem, and she retrieved the stapler from under the table to show me, a smug grimace on her face.

I didn't care if I was fired or not. But I really thought at that
moment that my half-finished Mediterranean ravioli article would
remain forever unfinished.

I really don't need this right now. Perhaps I should phone Dad and
tell him I'm ready for Mozambique this afternoon, then disappear to
India forever thereafter.

I stalked back to my desk and skulked behind my computer trying
desperately to focus on my rocket and stuffed figs feature. Needless
to say I subbed my own article that day.

GIULIA TIME

The curveballs keep coming. Giulia was up for the taking so we
slothed on the couch and shoved Pringles into our mouths. Later,

Giulia cooked us up some bella pasta and dished out advice.

'If your boss calls you in, just plead insanity. Has always worked for us Italians.'

'Should I pretend that I don't know what they're talking about?'

'Huh?'

'Should I pretend that ...'

'Huh? Huh geddit? Just say "huh?" every time they bring it up. And sub your own articles. Otherwise, she'll make you rewrite them a thousand times just for her own pleasure.'

'Okay, goddit.'

'I also think you must go to India. Then you won't need to bother with your boss and Evil Sub. Besides you're in love. And he loves you.'

'Well, that's pushing it.'

'No. We all know it, now shudda-uppa your face and eat your pasta.'

A YEAR OLDER

I am twenty-six today. Mortification.

Who knew that I'd be sitting here today and contemplating Connor as a, you know, *boyfriend*. I'm even considering flying across the world to see him. In the past, I'd just jump into something but this time I'm thinking carefully about what to do.

Break ups have made me stronger, if a little colder and harder. Lovers come and go, but friends and family stick with you even if you go psycho for a while. I'm a year older and I'm single. Instead of panicking, I am remaining calm. In fact, being twenty-six isn't so bad after all.

My close friends had a surprise birthday dinner party for me, which made me feel very loved. I arrived home from work and they all jumped out from behind the couch. Clichéd but cool. Giulia made pasta shaped like tiny penises, which everyone enjoyed. Everyone was there, i.e. The Most Hilarious People on the Planet. Bennet and I phoned Connor in India twice – and passed the phone around the table. Needless to say his phone bill will be horrendous. It was the first time Connor and I have spoken since The E-mail, but we both ignored it and, anyway, most of our conversation was alcohol-induced babble.

My folks even popped in for a drink and my mother started with, 'You know, Peas, now that you're twenty-six ...'

'Hold the phone right there. Almost twenty-six, Mum. I only turn twenty-six at 11:30 p.m.'

'Now that you're almost twenty-six, you have to start dressing more your age.'

My male friends flirted with my mother the entire evening, inducing her to wild giggles. Diego was particularly tactile, bringing her wine spritzers and trying his hand at speaking French. Although every time I came close he pretended he wasn't. My step-dad didn't seem to mind too much.

Sucked into my old lifestyle for one evening, I figured it was okay because 1) I have something to celebrate, and 2) I wasn't drowning my sorrows. I naturally ended up at Manhattan (it's been a while); I naturally ended up on Bennet's shoulders, and (whoops, this was a mistake) I (naturally?) kissed another Eastern Cape farmer.

What is up with that? He was actually very nice, even though he kept on saying 'You're crazy, man' over and over again. Lizzy needs to meet a farmer, not me. Do I look like someone who would milk cows? If I recall, I think Eastern Cape farmers have been the last three people I've shared saliva with. Besides, all I could think about was Connor. I will choose to forget this as quickly as it happened. A drunken, celebratory snog, that's all it was.

LIZZY: Oh. My. Shattered. Nerves. Can we be thee drunkest girls on the planet? I kissed my 'boyfriend'.

HELEN: 'I feel like Ghandi's slip-slop has taken residence in my mouth.'

BENNET: 'Have you seen my wallet?'

DIEGO: 'I'll pay anyone a hundred bucks to get me a babalas smoothie at Kauai.'

GIULIA: 'The penis pasta was a success!'

PEAS: 'I lunged an Eastern Cape farmer. Again.'

MUM: 'Diego tells me you use the Francophile card all the time. He did, however, have an awful lot to say about espetada basting sauces.'

Then on checking my sent items, *tres* important after a big night out:

PEAS: Liz did u score me i kissed eastern cape farmer new one bye.

LIZZY: I know. We all saw.

PEAS: Please don't tell Connor.

IF THERE'S ONE REASON TO GO TO INDIA ...

... it's so that I don't have to go into the office for a while.

My boss and The Sub are being remarkably quiet about The Incident. In fact, they're pretending that nothing happened. It's unnerving to say the least. But, I'm really not the one who should be embarrassed.

I'm still subbing my own articles; I can't take chances when I've basically witnessed Beezlebub giving the boss a blowjob. She offered to take a look at my '*Ratatouille de Bresson*' piece, almost kindly, but I distractedly said that she needn't. The boss even commented on how wonderful my 'Gazpacho Review of the World' was. He was so sweet, I was actually scared. What are the two of them planning? That clinched it for me. I will go to Mozambique with my father although I'm still undecided about India.

PEAS: 'Hi Dad.'

DAD: 'You're coming aren't you?'

PEAS: 'Well ...'

DAD: 'Excellent. I'll make sure all the nuts and bolts are in place for the trip.'

PEAS: 'That'll be especially relieving.'

DAD: 'What made you decide to come?'

PEAS: 'I wrongly sort of accused the sub-editor at work of giving my boss sexual favours. And I just need to get out of Jo'burg for a while. This place has become too much lately.'

DAD: 'Fair enough. Let me know when we can do it.'

AREN'T YOU MEANT TO BE MARRIED OR SOMETHING? I'm attending a school reunion tonight. It's not my ten-year reunion, which is most likely to be a huge affair involving trips down to Natal with a new wardrobe, a hired date, a new glamorous career and a fake wedding ring. Thank heavens not yet. I still have two years to attain all those things.

This is a little get together for all the ex-students living in Jozi now. My headmaster is supplying the drinks and snacks at a chosen venue. Is he out of his mind? He must have forgotten what kind of pupils we were. We're a close-knit bunch, us boarding school lot. I've remained good friends with many of my schoolmates, and he obviously has no idea that we get drunk together at least once a week. (Lizzy and Helen, for example, also went to school with us, but we've only really become friends over the last few months.)

We all met at Giles, an unpretentious yet fabulous little restaurant in Craighall Park. All I can really report is that we had too many tequilas, the headmaster was a scream, and he doesn't remember suspending me when I bunked out to see my boyfriend in Standard Nine.

Many of my classmates are either living with or getting married to their boyfriends. 'And you, Peas?'

'Nah. I'm pretty happy just being on my own.' I'm certain some envied me – because while they were whining about never finding a man, I was singing the praise of singledom – and actually meaning it. Until Lizzy announced to everyone: 'She's lying. Her soul mate is currently trying to woo her to India. They're in love, but she refuses to admit it.'

I shot her an annoyed look. 'Lizzy, don't be ridiculous. India? Pah.'

HELEN: 'Peas, it's the most romantic non-love story *I've* ever heard. Don't you ladies all agree?'

Heads wagged in unison, they all clucked appreciatively, and wanted to know who Connor was, why on earth he's living in India in the first place, and why I was even hesitating.

I ordered a round of tequilas to shut them up. Those desperate to get married and have babies can be awfully convincing but I didn't want to talk about it. This is a decision I need to make on my own.

LIZZY: 'Say you'll only go if he gets you a part in a Bollywood film.'

HELEN: 'Maybe he'll take you to the Taj Mahal?'

PEAS: 'What part of "I don't want to talk about this with you guys" don't you understand?'

That's said, I can't deny that I'm stuck on something. And that something is a certain dark-haired, blue-eyed semi-Irishman currently living in Delhi.

A PASSAGE TO INDIA

I confided in Lizzy exactly how I'm feeling about Connor. Until now, she's made her own assumptions, and I've never denied or substantiated them. I didn't plan to divulge all, but after dragging me to a crazy party, and after many a drink was drunk, it all came out, that I might be in love with him. I've finally admitted this to myself. When I can tell her sober, then I'll make a decision on whether to go to India to meet up with him. Until then, the decision is still pending.

LIZZY: 'I know this. You don't need to tell me. Best friends know this stuff.'

PEAS: 'I know you know, but I'm admitting to you that *maybe,* just maybe, I know now.'

LIZZY: 'Well then we'd better celebrate, hadn't we?'

PEAS: 'Wait. You're not seeing anyone at the moment are you? Tell me everything.'

LIZZY: 'No, Peas. I'm not. I do like that you asked though. I did however find this burly man at this party last week, and ...'

This is me packing.

Dad has given me his grace that I'm allowed to bring toiletries on this trip. However, I'm only allowed two changes of clothes, which I shall need to wash. *Is he kidding me?*

And now he's sprung it on me that it's not only me and him going. This is the very reason for lack of luggage space in the Cessna. He's hired a bloody co-pilot.

DAD: 'He'll make sure we get there in one piece. He's very thorough, Peas.'

PEAS: 'I thought this was a father-daughter trip.'

DAD: 'It is! He keeps to himself anyway, being German and all.'

PEAS: 'Whatever. Fine.'

DAD: 'His name is Voltah. Be polite. He trained in Düsseldorf.'

PEAS: 'Voltah as in Walter? If he pulls a zeitgeist, regimented no-sense-of-humour thing on this trip, Dad, I'll be very sulky.'

GOODBYE SUB-EDITOR D'HELL

As I was saying *adios* to the office, The Sub picked up the stapler again today and attended to my boss' wayward trouser seams presumably just to make a point.

Dad's picking me up in two hours. We're flying out of Brakpan and heading to Vilankulos. The aircraft is small and needs refuelling after every two hours of flying. I suppose this means I get regular smoke and pee breaks on the journey towards the Mozambican coastline. The luggage compartment is simply stowage space behind the seats. I had to sort out my own life jacket from Cape Union Mart beforehand.

Voltah is your classic, if not bossy, German who insisted I take my heels off for the trip to Vilankulos. He is insanely attractive and dashing and paid me lots of attention, but spending eight hours in a tiny Cessna with him got me thinking only about one person: Connor.

When he used to shed his clothes at the end of a party, I didn't openly ogle his member. But now, the very picture of Connor's penis spent a great deal of time bouncing around my head during the trip. Even if Voltah's mono-chromatic voice kept on breaking my reverie and Dad phoned up all his mates from the cockpit on his cellular phone. I didn't care. I had made a decision.

Once on the lush shores of balmy Vilankulos, I dropped my bags in my little beach cottage and – in heels on the soft sand – ran to find an Internet café:

From: peasontoast@gmail.com
To: connor@irishcarbomb.com
Subject: I'm in Mozambique

Okay, I've barely stepped out the tiny vomit comet since we took off out of Brakpan, I haven't had a chance to smell the sea air or feel the relief of being out of Jo'burg for a few days. I'm sitting in a beach Internet café in my heels and pencil skirt, surrounded by bronzed, dreadlocked hippies writing to you. Honestly, I haven't I've even dipped my hairy toes in the sea yet.

I'm coming over to India, Connor. And we have lots to talk about. I've thought about this long and hard and have come to this decision on my own. I do love you. As more than a friend. It takes guts to say this (because the last time I told someone, he ran from my house) but I know it's all right because you feel the same way. So, clean your house, attend to the dirty dishes and make space for my suitcase, I'm flying over.

Love,
Peas

DAD AND I BOND

After much botheration with the intermittent Internet connection at the Baobab Bar, I finally booked my flight to New Delhi.

Then Dad and I sat on the beach, waves lapping at our feet and shared a joint. Seeing my father stoned is unsettling. Usually his concentration levels span about five seconds, but stoned he completely loses the plot. However, if this meant he was going to open up and talk to me, then by all means, he should indulge.

In his opinion, my job at *Good Food* magazine was fantastic, even if The Sub did sexual things with my boss. ('Hell, my old editor in London used to throw things at me if I didn't come back with top photos. You have it good, my girl.')

PEAS: 'Sometimes I wonder whether you're consciously present.'
DAD: 'Really?'
PEAS: 'Yip. I can be similar actually. Maybe I get it from you.' I punched him lightly on the shoulder and gave him a hug.
DAD: 'I'm not really all that bad, am I, Peas?'
PEAS: 'I know you're not perfect, Dad. And I love you for being different. You have to do what makes you happy, Dad. And maybe many girlfriends isn't the answer either.'
DAD: 'Perhaps not.'

PEAS: 'I understand wanting to escape. It eventually catches up with you though.'

DAD: 'So tell me about this Colin guy.'

PEAS: 'Well ... Colin is ...'

I told him about Connor as we sat together on the beach. And for the first time for as long as I could remember, he listened. Attentively with no interruptions, no flying off on tangents about himself or nothing in particular. He put in an astounding effort.

DAD: 'Is this Connie person a guy? Ooh, look at the pretty dhow crossing the bay. Sorry. Okay, I'm listening.'

PEAS: 'Connor. You'll find he has a guy name too.'

DAD: 'You off to India for good? Don't do that, Peas. I don't want you in some cult.'

PEAS: 'I'll be back. I need to do this, Dad.'

DAD: 'And all the bastards you've cried over?'

PEAS: 'I suppose I had to cry over them to get where I am now. God only knows life isn't a smooth ride for the guy who chooses to be with me. What scares and awes me at the same time is how I am so much like you.'

DAD: 'Sheesh, I'm hungry. I could murder a plate of prawns right now.'

Then I listened to him. About loving a woman who was not his wife.

PEAS: 'Dad, why did you leave Mum like that? Just left her?'

DAD: 'I handled things the wrong way, Peas. That I can't deny. I was selfish and didn't think of the consequences.'

PEAS: 'Do you regret it?'

DAD: 'I regret how I did it, yes. It was humiliating and awful for her. But it was something I had to do. I'm just so sorry for the hurt I caused.'

PEAS: 'I forgive you, Dad. I do.'

DAD: 'Just remember, that a man must commit to you, my darling, with his full heart.'

Tears welled up, I gave him a hug and we walked in silence along the beach.

I then returned to the Internet café to find an e-mail from Connor. My legs were noodles, my stomach was a washing machine:

> From: connor@irishcarbomb.com
> To: peasontoast@gmail.com
> Subject: I am unbelievably ...
>
> (Unbelievably what? Just torture me in the subject line, why don't you.)
>
> ... ecstatic. Your e-mail made me jump around my tiny house, put Keane into the CD player and rip open a can of beer, because your e-mail, my darling Peas, has made my night. My year. Before I bore you with questions as to when you're coming, I also want to clarify my thoughts. Confessing my undying love for my best girl friend took a lot of balls too, you know! Oh there you have it, whoops, confessed. I am so very much in love with you, Peas. You obliterate every other thought, I miss you like nothing on earth, please come over as soon as you can possibly find a ticket out. Just get here.
>
> Tell Lizzy and Giulia thanks for working on you. They're wise women, those two. Of course I'm in love with you. Let's not waste one more minute.
>
> Connor xxxxxxxxxxxxxxxxxxxxxxxxxxxxxxxxxxx (and more when you get here)

Be still, my quaking heart. Could this be possibly the most romantic e-mail I have ever received? Overwhelmed by lust, adoration, infatuation and love, I walked along the beach. I'm still perplexed – how has this all happened? Was it destiny all along?

Later, I encountered a gorgeous English creature at the prawn buffet over dinner. I penned a letter to him, because I couldn't sleep:

Dear Attractive Man From Coventry
Tonight, after dinner with Dad, who I think ate 534 tiger prawns and drank far too many rum cocktails, I fell into bed, head spinning and thought about you as I drifted off to sleep.

You are the extremely attractive man I met at the buffet cart. An Englishman. Now most Englishmen leave me weak at the knees if they so much as utter a sentence in their little accents (barring Essex and Cockney), but you were simply delicious. Older, perhaps mid-thirties, maybe even forty, who knows.

The way you wrapped your mouth around the word 'Coventry' (where you were born?) and how you told me about driving from Maputo to Nampula in a Chevy Spark ... Well, you really were quite lovely.

Naturally you had a wedding ring on your left hand, probably have offspring and live in the UK. And I'm hoping to start seeing someone. Hell, I am seeing someone, aren't I? But I won't bore you with the details.

Pardon? I am sort of seeing someone. *Yes I am. Writing down this suddenly not-so-single-anymore status has completely taken me by surprise. It's finally sunk in: I will be completely and utterly not single anymore. So, I suppose I'm not really on the market at this precise moment. I know I've been in a fair bit of denial recently, but I since I chose not to flirt the pants off you (a very attractive, upstanding suit-wearing, dark and rugged married man from Coventry) it's really hit home. My mind and heart belong to someone.*

Yours in India rather than in the English countryside,
Peas on Toast

NEW ADVENTURE, NEW PLACE, NEW LOVE

Dad has decided to stay in Vilankulos. I wish I could've spent more time with him but we've certainly made progress. It was a tearful goodbye but I know he'll be fine since meeting Carol in the cocktail bar yesterday evening, who looks rather striking in a sarong, if I do say so myself. We bear hugged for five whole minutes. He stroked my hair and promised that he was just a phone call away if I ever needed him to 'pop a cap in Connor'.

I called my friends to tell them the news and cried some more. Giulia tut-tutted and Lizzy said she'd never forgive me if I decided to have a Hindu wedding without her being there. Diego asked if he could tag along on the trip. (I said *nao*. No in Portuguese.) My mother sounded delighted on the other end of the receiver, admitting that Connor was always her favourite boy – apparently even her sound vibration healing club had bets on when we'd get together. (Tessa owes her R200.) And lastly, I called work and told The Sub to tell the boss that I wouldn't be back for a while. 'How long exactly? Just who do you think you are, Peas?' I told her to have a pleasant day at work and rang off. If my job is there when I get back, so be it. If not, the world won't stop rotating.

After catching a flight back to Jo'burg, I waited in the departure lounge for my one-way flight to New Delhi. It's a crazy thing to do, I know. It could be a massive mistake. But my head is clearer than it's been in a long time and I'm running with my instincts, jumping on an international flight to test the water out with someone. Except it's not just someone, it's Connor and investing hope in him isn't a leap of faith, it's somehow natural.

And so, the Beginning.

Acknowledgements

My novel wouldn't have been possible without Blogger.com, Peas On Toast and Pan Macmillan. The book's inception, and tuning thereof, would never have occurred without my experienced, funky sidekick and editor, Nikki Temkin. ('I thought I just lost the latest draft. Ja. Am sweating buckets.') Nikki, Jonathan and Terry, thank you for working on this project with me over the last three years.

For the people that have always believed in me, my friends, family, late guinea pig, the French, the person who thought mixing red paint with white paint would result in a cool colour, hot-looking geeks. To my loyal blog readers' and to the people that have inspired some of these characters.

Thank you.
LAURIAN CLEMENCE